IDELETTE

Idelette de Bure

IDELETTE

A NOVEL BASED ON THE
LIFE OF MADAME JOHN CALVIN

by
EDNA GERSTNER

Author of
Song by the River

Soli Deo Gloria Publications
...for instruction in righteousness...

Soli Deo Gloria Publications
213 W. Vincent Street, Ligonier, PA 15658
(412) 238-7741

*

Idelette was first published in 1963 by
Zondervan Publishing House
Grand Rapids, Michigan.
This Soli Deo Gloria reprint is 1992.

*

ISBN 1-877611-54-9
Library of Congress
Catalog Card Number 63-9313

*To my husband, a professor of church history,
without whose help this novel would have
been much more interesting — but
far less accurate.*

IDELETTE

1

"I know just the girl you ought to marry," Pastor Martin Bucer spoke with conviction.

"What, another one?" was the unenthusiastic reaction of his bachelor friend, Jean Calvin. But he smiled as he said it Jean Calvin had never know happier days than his early ones in the city of Strasbourg where, beaten in body and spirit from his ordeal in Geneva, he had been persuaded to come as pastor of the little refugee church of Saint Nicolas. He had been persuaded by the very man who was now urging him to another major decision.

Bucer had written stormily to him, when h had been reluctant to come, "God will know how to find the rebellious servant, as He found Jonah." The "rebellious servant" had come, and with many another had known true hospitality in the Bucer home — the "Inn of Righteousness," the people called it. And now Calvin knew that Martin's strong desire for him to marry grew from his own happy marriage and his wish that his friend also enjoy this blessing. Still, not overlooking the good motives of his friend, Jean Calvin could not resist the jab.

"Now, Jean. You must not blame me for the last girl that was proposed to you. I always thought she was too young. It was your brother, Antoine, and Claude. . . ."

"Whose lack of discernment almost succeeded in marrying me to a woman of loose morals."

9

"She loved the other man, Jean. She is going to marry him."

"Then why, may I ask, did she consent to marry me while carrying on a relationship with a man she loved? Or is my question too illogical?"

"Illogical? You, Jean Calvin!" Martin's eyes twinkled. "But this woman is quite different. . . ."

"They have all been — all the preceding women you have brought to my attention as possibilities for my hand in marriage."

"We have not had too great success in the past. But will you not at least consider this one? You know I am acting only out of my concern and deep affection for you."

"Then out of that deep affection, please, Martin, no more loves. Come let us talk of pleasanter things. How did you find Pierre Viret . . . ?"

"But the Widow Stordeur — "

"Did you say the Widow Stordeur?"

Sensing a quickening of interest, Martin Bucer, the great persuader, took full advantage of the moment. In his usual methodical fashion he had come fully prepared to do so. He pulled a piece of paper out of his pocket and energetically proceeded to enumerate the lady's virtues, which he had listed seriatim.

"1. She is pious.

2. She is no young inexperienced girl. She has already proved that she can be a virtuous wife — you see how unlike she is to the last one.

3. Although most of her life has been spent in Belgium, she is French by birth, having been born, like you, in Picardy. French is her native tongue. You cannot discard this one, for reasons of language.

4. She comes from a respected family.

5. She is quiet.

6. She is modest.

7. She is beautiful.

8. She is a good mother to her two fatherless children.

9. She is a faithful church member of your own parish.

10. She would give her consent."

"Enough! Enough! Your decalogue is very convincing, my friend — especially the last argument," Jean Calvin added wryly. "You have my blessing for the wooing."

Martin Bucer was pleasantly surprised at his easy victory, but also a little disappointed. He felt like a man who has braced his shoulders to break down a door only to find it swing open even as he charged. He had scarcely begun to fight. Immodestly he took more credit than he should have for his own powers of persuasion.

2

Almost afraid to believe that his easy victory over his friend's reluctance to marry would last, Martin Bucer, a practical man, decided to waste no time in fulfilling his commission to be the go-between in the courtship of Jean Calvin and Idelette Stordeur. He was not wholly easy about his visit, for he realized that when speaking to Jean Calvin about her he had allowed himself to be carried away by the enthusiasm of the moment, and had exceeded the confines of strict truth when he had assured his friend that the widow would assuredly give her consent. Point number 10, she being a sensible woman, he had merely assumed.

But though his mind was burdened with some difficulties which would perhaps be facing him, as he picked his way through the narrow streets past the great Gothic Cathedral of Strasbourg, his overall mood was jubilant. He found himself pausing in his walk, as always, to admire this masterpiece of religious architecture. His own church had, in the Protestant tradition of the day, stripped away in the the interior all images, altars, anything reminiscent of the Romish tradition. Its outside architecture had little to redeem it, for it was a small gray stone church; and much as he loved it, any honest man had to admit that it was drab and ugly by comparison. Its squat tower did not do for the soul what this beautiful lacy tower did, pointing gloriously four hundred and fifty feet upward to God.

In spite of his Reformation antipathy for imagery, his personal revolt — for he had been a Dominican monk — Bucer was not totally blind to the fact that sermons could be told in stone, and the great doors of the cathedral depicting the great themes of sin and redemption never failed to make an impact upon him.

Today he stood noticing particularly the first door nearest him, where was etched the gospel story of the youth of Christ. The artist had caught magnificently the two natures of Christ, man and God, evident even in the young Christ Jesus. Bucer was chastened when he saw the statues of the Cardinal Virtues and the seven Christian Virtues. It was only as his eyes fell on the statue of the Wise Virgin that he was abruptly recalled to his errand.

Idelette Stordeur had something in common with the face of a Mary on the cathedral door. The carver had sculptured a serenity, a depth of compassion which only suffering can bring, on the Madonna's face. Martin Bucer had always noticed this same rare look on Idelette. It was not so much what was sculptured but an absence of line. Greed, pride, the common vices were not there. This made it so striking. A lack of etching of these vices, an almost blankness of face — this it was which captured the imagination. Unlike his friend, Jean Calvin, Martin Bucer did not find this quality disquieting.

He was thinking of these qualities which he believed Idelette possessed as he hurried on his way. After the death of Jean Stordeur, his widow and two children had of necessity moved from their own modest house into one small room in the home of Idelette's brother, Charles de Bure. At that time the de Bure family, Charles and his wife Antoinette and their two children, were living on a narrow street beyond the Cathedral, almost as far as the church of Saint Nicolas, the Petite Eglise, which lay near the South wall.

The house, typical of the well-to-do middle class of the day, was choicely but sparsely furnished. Monsieur Bucer was ushered into a living room and shown to one of the few chairs. Madame de Bure was obviously flustered to see the noted Pastor of St. Thomas in her home. She fumbled with the wire circlets and tampons over which her hair was drawn to give the fashionably desired width of forehead. Not a hair was out of place. It was purely a gesture of nervousness.

"Pray be seated, Monsieur le Curé. If I had known you were coming, I would have made the room more ready. . . ."

There was no need for an apology. Madame de Bure, like all Strasbourg housewives, was a spotless housekeeper and extremely tidy about her own person, and that of her family. Monsieur Bucer sat down, as delicately as his own bulk would allow, in the fragile carved chair indicated. He only hoped he would not repay the honor shown him by smashing the legs upon which it stood. Strasbourg cleanliness was no new thing to him. His own Elizabeth was extremely fastidious. How she was able to keep his large and well-filled home so immaculate was to him somewhat of a minor miracle. He was aware, however, that she worked at it. For there were those moments when it would be, "Martin, did you scrape your boots as you came in?" Elizabeth, herself, always wore pattens over her shoes for outdoor wear, and the soft undershoes never left a mark. He sighed. This was one virtue, he reflected, he hoped Idelette did not possess to excess.

He smiled reassuringly at his flustered hostess and asked, "Is your sister-in-law, Madame Stordeur, at home?"

"Yes, Monsieur."

"Would you please ask her to come in? I should like very much to see her alone. It is a matter of great privacy."

Madame de Bure did not betray any curiosity at his errand, and Martin, who was no stranger to the nature of women, began to be assured that the purpose of his visit would after all not be too much of a surprise. He calmed himself by thinking of scriptural analogies relevant to his somewhat delicate mission. He was comparing himself, in his own mind, to the very successful servant of Abraham when

Idelette entered. She walked so quietly he did not notice her entrance until she stood before him, so like the statue on the Strasbourg Cathedral that he found himself for once at a loss for words. She stood so still, as almost not to be alive. He shook himself loose from the fantasy that he was speaking to an image. His customary courtesy helped to make a beginning.

"Pray be seated, Madame."

Idelette sat down on one of the remaining chairs. Martin could not escape noticing how gracefully even this common act was accomplished. She tucked her small feet under the hem of her long skirt and looked up at him from under the little lace cap she had worn — for him, no doubt. The little cap came down to a point in the center of the forehead. Thus framed, the lady's oval face looked heart-shaped. Martin found himself warming to his task.

He cleared his throat. "You are well, Madame?"

"Yes, thank you."

"And the children . . . ?"

"They are well, too."

He cleared his throat again. Thrusting aside as unworthy any further desire to postpone his mission, and the amenities he felt accomplished, he began, "I have come to see you today, Madame, on a very important errand. No man has ever been an emissary on a task which is more pleasant for him. Perhaps I should have spoken to your brother rather than to you; but you are a mature woman and accustomed to making your own decisions."

He coughed again. She sat very still. Her big eyes showed no awareness of his role. He saw only courtesy and certainly no anticipation or encouragement in them. "Monsieur Calvin, your pastor, is not a well man, as you know. He often suffers from difficulty in breathing, and is more often than is known laid up with the gout. He will not spare himself, and many of us fear for his health. He is indispensable to the great Christian world. I do not exaggerate when I say I myself believe that his is the greatest voice for God today."

His cramped position on the delicate chair was hampering Martin Bucer's efforts. That, together with the quietly motionless Idelette, was undermining his eloquence. Abruptly he rose and paced back and forth before the seated Idelette. He paused suddenly and whirled around and said to her, "Do you not think so?"

"My husband often said those very words, Monsieur le Curé."

It was not quite the answer Martin Bucer wanted. He tried again, "We all want to see his life prolonged, do we not?"

"Yes, Monsieur."

"And we will all do anything in our power to accomplish this?"

"Yes, Monsieur."

Martin Bucer sighed with relief. "I am so grateful that you agree with me. Then it is all settled."

"What is settled, Monsieur?"

"Is it not obvious? Your marriage to Monsieur Jean Calvin."

Another woman would have expostulated. Idelette did not betray by the slightest gesture how great was her astonishment. If possible, she became even quieter than before. It was Martin Bucer who spoke again, "Did you not hear me, Madame?"

"Yes, Monsieur. It is just that I thought Monsieur Calvin was to marry —"

Martin was embarrassed that she had known of the incident. He did not let her finish her sentence. "No, no, Madame, that is at an end. It was a most unfortunate alliance from the beginning. The girl was quite unsuitable. She was never my choice. Now you, you will be a very fitting wife. You have been married once before, and your experience will help. You will know how to make Monsieur Calvin comfortable —"

"I do not wish to make Monsieur Calvin comfortable," Idelette calmly interrupted.

Martin Bucer could not believe his ears. Up until this moment he thought that the interview had been going very well.

"I have been married once before. I am experienced. You are right." She continued slowly, "It was a happy and fortunate marriage. I do not wish to marry again." Her voice rebuked him, "One does not marry to give comfort, Monsieur."

Martin Bucer regretted that he had not let his wife, Elizabeth, handle this. But now that he was in it, he plunged doggedly on, "What basis do you suggest for marriage, Madame?"

Idelette fixed her eyes on him, "Was it for your comfort that Madame Bucer married you?" She spoke gently. "We all know of the happiness you enjoy. I do not mean to say that it is not a wife's duty to give comfort, but surely there must first be a mutual esteem — "

"Ah! I have fumbled badly. That is what I meant to say." He pressed the advantage her answer gave him, "You do hold Monsieur Calvin in esteem?"

"Very much."

"Then you see, you have your esteem, and he has a great need for a good wife — for comfort, I repeat, Madame."

"Does it follow that I should be the source of this comfort?"

"He admires you greatly."

"Did Monsieur Calvin say so?"

In all honesty, Martin Bucer could not answer. He began to wish he had come prepared with a sheet of paper, an itemized list of arguments, for this interview also. His easy victory with Jean Calvin had been his downfall. Who would have thought so quiet a woman would be so difficult? But spontaneous urgings came to him, and he became flushed with the earnestness of his pleadings.

The whole interview lasted an hour. During it Idelette

hardly contributed a sentence. But before he left, Martin Bucer had at least succeeded in extracting from Madame Stordeur the promise to give the matter prayerful consideration. She would give him her final answer within the week. Wiping his forehead, Martin Bucer left, only too glad to leave the matter in the hands of the Almighty.

As soon as he left, Madame de Bure hurried back into the room.

"Why did he come, sister?"

Idelette's eyes were reproachful. "I think perhaps you know. What did you and Madame Bucer have your heads together about the other day?"

Madame de Bure hung her head. "It would be a wonderful alliance."

"Did you lead Madame Bucer to think I would be willing?"

"I made no commitments. But I did think. . . . What answer did you give?"

"I could give no answer."

"Because of Jean Stordeur."

"Yes, because of Jean."

"Jean is dead."

"Is he?" answered Idelette. . . .

Idelette sat on a low three-legged stool beside her husband's pallet. The bodice of her plain green dress was splotched with blood, and a fresh stain was spreading slowly down her full skirt. She noticed it only when it reached her thin silk house slippers. She tensed and tucked her feet more firmly beneath her. The rest of her body remained stiff and motionless, alert for the sick man's next awful retching. Only her eyes moved, recoiling with each desperate convulsion of the dying man.

The big hairy chest heaved ceaselessly with the effort of breathing, and rivers of sweat drenched the linens almost as soon as they were changed. The face was bloated and almost unrecognizable. Idelette had seen for the first time today, starting at the throat, the dreaded small blue plague spots that blotted out hope.

Now and then, automatically, she rose, and going to the basin which she had placed on a low table near the pallet, she soaked a cloth in the cool water and washed his body. Or, wetting a small rag, she tried to moisten his fuzzy red-tipped tongue which was so swollen it was forcing his cracked lips apart. She knew the dryness he was suffering must be torment. At moments like this his bloodshot eyes would follow her unexpected motions, but when she looked at them she saw they were vacant and glazed. Already for him she had ceased to exist.

Idelette wanted to run, to flee from this room of pestilence. She was conscious that it was spring. Her tulips were in bloom. The sun was shining. But she was afraid even to open a window to let in the fresh sweet fragrance of spring. And she stayed inside shut in with death and decay and a stranger lying wide-eyed on his bed — a stranger who had been her husband. She sat firmly on her stool, and folded her hands in her lap, and waited.

For three days she fought sleep. She must have dozed, for when she awakened a shadow lay across the pallet. Her eyes, always big and wide, were now enormous with fatigue. She had trouble focusing.

"You need sleep, Madame Stordeur." A voice spoke gently. "Go to your room. Let me keep your vigil for a time."

She recognized that voice. "He is my husband. I cannot leave. It is my duty to stay."

"He is my friend. Will you not let me help?"

But she would not yield her place. Seeing he was defeated in his good intentions, the visitor stepped past her and knelt down by the pallet. Taking the big hairy hand into his own slender long fingers, he began to pray.

"Almighty God, Redeemer of Thy people, we commit the soul of this Thy child into Thy safe keeping. . . ." Idelette stirred. He prayed for her and the children. "Oh, kind

and compassionate Saviour, the Source of all tenderness. . . ."
The melodious voice went on; but her numbed brain only
caught at fragments of words. "Sins . . . Grace . . . The glory
of Thy presence. . . . In Jesus' name we pray, Amen."

The prayer ended, the man rose from his knees, and
turned to face the woman who was so still.

"It will be over soon, and he will be with his Redeemer."

The face she lifted to him was beautiful but inscrutable.
He felt uncomfortable looking at it.

"The children?" He ventured.

"Are with my brother."

"They are safe then."

"Yes."

"God's hand, which rests heavy upon you in this hour,
is the same hand which has blessed you with them."

"Yes."

A silence fell between them. Again he felt ill at ease,
almost irritated by the silence. He wished she would say
something. Hysterical grief he knew how to handle, but
this strange quietness.

Then she spoke at length, and it moved him that it
was of him she thought. "You should not have come into this
house of death. Jean would not have permitted it if he had
known. I have been so slow, so dulled by grief. I should
have barred your way." She stood before him. "You are
too valuable to the work — "

He did not let her finish. "I am his pastor and his
friend. It is my duty to come, my duty to God."

"Thank you," she said simply. "Thank you, for Jean
and for myself, Monsieur Calvin." She bent her head and
kissed his hand.

He felt embarrassed, touched and awkward. Abruptly
he left the room. Idelette Stordeur went back to her stool,
sat down, crossed her feet beneath her again, and waited.

3

"I don't want him for a father," Charles said indignantly.

Idelette closed the window shutters and turned to face her angry young son.

"Uncle Charles says you are going to marry Monsieur Jean Calvin. I do not want him for a father," he repeated with heat.

"Why not, my child?" Idelette spoke so quietly it was necessary to strain to hear her. "He is a good man, and he was your father's friend."

Judith sat primly on her small stool, her wide skirt spread out neatly about her, and watched the scene with complete detachment. People said of her that she was a strange child, solemn beyond her years. She was, in truth, her mother's child.

Charles, on the other hand, was very like his dead father — handsome, tempestuous, affectionate; but unlike his father he had not yet learned to control his passionate nature. Those who had known the elder Stordeur only superficially had felt him to be a brutish man. His huge bulk was apt to mislead one. But those who knew his work in wood and ivory, the intricate carvings which his large hands accomplished, realized his was a nature which had learned patience, discipline and the importance of painstaking perfection.

21

Idelette had never so much noticed the resemblance to his father that her son Charles bore in the days since Jean's death. This likeness troubled her now as she watched her son in his open defiance.

"You need a father, Charles. These are very hard days for a boy with only a woman to care for him."

"Then choose another. No good woman marries a priest." He flung at her the common slur of the streets. She hit him across the cheek with the flat of her hand. The boy shrank — not so much at the blow, as at the sight of the perpetual calm of his mother shattered before him. He was afraid.

"Never," her voice became a whisper, "never let me hear you speak like that again. The woman who marries Monsieur Calvin will not be disgraced, but will be highly honored to share his destiny. Believe me, my son, he is a man of destiny; his is a voice that will affect not only our generation but all ages. Try to understand." She put her arms around the angry boy; but he broke away, and left the room in tears.

"And you, Judith, what do you think about my marrying Monsieur Calvin?" The girl had not stirred during the quarrel. She answered the question in the way Idelette expected she would, "I should like very much for Monsieur le Curé to be my new papa."

Idelette looked uneasily at her. Unreasonably she wished Judith, for once, had sided with her brother, had taken an unpleasant position. Her daughter always sought to give the answer that would please.

Idelette walked back to the shuttered window and rested her head against the cool wood. She was tormented by the decision she must make. Should she marry again? Could she when Jean Stordeur so much filled her mind? Was he dead for her, enough that she could let another man take his place?

She indulged herself in memories. She remembered her courtship days in Liege, Belgium. How happy they had been with each other. What happiness their marriage had brought them. How they had rejoiced when their two children had been given them. Even in the hard lean years of refugee life they had known the deeper joy of sharing hardship and poverty together, and the triumph of knowing that their union was strong enough to surmount months of hunger and persecution. Ironically, some of this persecution had come indirectly from the hand of Jean Calvin. For both she and Jean Stordeur had been Anabaptists; and only after much time and study had her husband and finally she been persuaded of the Reformed position. Once again it had been Jean Calvin who had played the leading role. He had been the one who had converted her husband. And never had she known anyone whom Jean Stordeur admired as he did that frail pastor of Strasbourg. Would it not be easier for her to marry someone whose life had not been so intricately woven already with her own — one perhaps who could not arouse memories of her dead husband?

And how well did she know Monsieur Calvin, the man? She had sat in his church and heard him preach. It had been almost a year now. She had heard him discuss theology with her husband on his visits to her home. As a theologian she knew his virtues; but as a human being? She knew he was often sick — irritable, some people said. Monsieur Bucer felt that it was her duty to marry him in order to take care of him. But what if this care conflicted with her duty to her own children? This situation was now aggravated by Charles' stubborn opposition. Should she override it, feeling that in the end her son would be greatly benefited by the firm hand of a godly father in the home? How difficult her decision was. Could she win Charles? If one could only foresee the future.

And what of Monsieur Calvin's mode of life? She knew he was very poor. It was a known fact that his salary was meagre, and half the time the city of Strasbourg forgot to pay it. He had to take in pensioners to board in his home to manage a livelihood. Could he assume the added bur-

den of a widow with two young children? Could she pay
her own way? And how would she fit into his strange household? In his rented house lived his brother Antoine, several men students, a housekeeper (the reputation of whose
shrewish tongue had reached even Idelette), and the housekeeper's indulged son. Her mind was in a tumult.

But her daughter saw nothing of this in her face, nothing but the usual calm of her mother. The days were almost
used up of the week Monsieur Bucer had allowed for her
final decision. Only one day, the Sabbath Day, remained,
for on Monday Monsieur Bucer was coming for his answer.

"I'm hungry, Mother. It is growing late. Why don't
we eat?" Judith complained.

"We shall, at once. It is late, my daughter, very, very
late."

4

Early Sabbath morning Idelette prepared for church. Her mind was still undecided. Yet her own heart felt a new excitement as she dressed for the service and she realized for the first time the new significance the man in the pulpit would have for her.

It was her custom to complete her own toilet before letting the children begin. She chose this morning to wear an underskirt of deep purple. The overskirt, which fell open all the way down the front, was of a lavender shade. The pointed bodice was lavender embroidered with deep purple. Embroidery was one of Idelette's pastimes, and what the material lacked in quality was compensated for by the beautiful handwork. Around her tiny waist she wore the girdle which was a necessary part of the dress of both sexes of the day. From it hung her house keys, her purse, and her Bible. Idelette did not tighten her waist with the wooden splints so many of the women used. She did not even wear a leather corset. A slender waist, perhaps the greatest to be desired beauty mark of the period, was hers by nature. She took special care as she rolled up her long thick dark hair into a great coil and piled it high on her head. Her small, tight-fitting Dutch cap would cover the front. She carefully arranged her coif of embroidered lawn to fall in even folds.

After preparing herself she dressed Judith. Charles

always had to wait until the end. He was so restless that if she started with him — even though he was now ten — he would look untidy the moment her back was turned. Judith, although younger than her brother, could be counted on to sit still and stay unmussed. Today the little girl wore a dress, a tiny rose duplicate of her mother's, which Idelette had made for her.

With Judith ready, Idelette told Charles to start dressing. For once he was sitting patiently, waiting his turn, dressed only in his tights — a snug garment which covered him from his waist to his feet. His mother had laid out his clothes for him. First he put on the shirt she had made of holland lawn. It had the stylish low neckline of the day, with sleeves full and loose to the wrist. Over this the young boy put on his doublet. This was sleeveless and padded and reached to the waist. Next went his jerkin, trimmed with narrow black bands. Most of the time Charles wore clogs on his feet; but his Uncle Charles had given him a pair of leather shoes for Sunday wear. These were like mules, without any heels. Since he was still a boy he wore, instead of the adult beret, a small bonnet with a plume.

Idelette felt a surge of maternal pride when she looked at the children. Charles, especially, carried himself with such liveliness that most heads turned to watch him. The family usually looked forward to the Sabbath walk to the Petite Eglise of Saint Nicolas. They would leave enough of a time margin to permit sauntering the long way around, crossing the long winding wooden bridge over the Ill river. They would take crumbs of bread and stop to feed the swans. But today even the lovely birds failed to change the mood of depression which, rooted in Charles, had spread over them all. The swans were neglected. Charles' handsome face remained drawn up in the scowl which had become almost a permanent expression on him this past week.

Idelette herself was nervous. As they walked up the narrow cobble-stoned street and began to near the church, on the Rue de Bouclier, friends joined them. All spoke the

soft tongue of the French. Idelette spoke German also;
but she and Jean, although not French refugees, had felt
more at home in the French Refugee Church than in the
German Church of St. Thomas.

As they passed the house where Monsieur Calvin
roomed, Idelette found herself taking a new interest in it.
It was an ugly oblong building with eight front windows.
All were shuttered, and one of the shutters rattled in the
breeze and hung awry. It offended Idelette's housewifely
instincts to hear it banging in the wind. She stole a back-
ward look, and then ashamed at her secular thoughts, she
hurried the children along.

Once inside the church of Saint Nicolas, she and the
children slipped into their side benches as inconspicuously
as possible. There seemed to be a rustle of interest in her
and her family in the nearest pews, or was she imagining it?
She only hoped her sister-in-law had not confided the news
to too many. She and the children stood with bowed heads
for a moment of silent prayer, and then sat down. Charles
had not yet lost the sullen look on his face. Judith placidly
stared back at her neighbors. Idelette sat looking at her
lap. It was unusual for her to feel nervous. She was grateful for the bell which tolled the beginning of the service.

From the side door Monsieur Calvin entered. His long
black robe gave him added height and dignity. He walked
with a grace unusual for a man. She lowered her eyes as
he reached the pulpit and turned to face his congregation.
She kept her eyes lowered through the Invocation and the
Announcement of Absolution to all who repent and seek
Jesus Christ for their salvation. But as the congregation
started to sing the first four commandments of the Decalogue
she raised her eyes. Jean Calvin's penetrating eyes were
fixed on her. She had known they would be. She did not
drop her own eyes, and it was he who first turned away.

She had not meant to outstare him. He looked pallid —
more so than usual — and there were dark smudges of
fatigue under his eyes. Monsieur Bucer had told her he

was not well. Perhaps his pallor was merely the result of another of his many sleepless nights; or maybe the cause of it was the nervous indigestion with which he was afflicted. She was too honest to dismiss the possibility that her hesitation at marriage had caused him distress. She had heard that any vital decision upset him physically. Had she made him ill?

How different he was from Jean Stordeur. In Belgium they had called Jean the "ox." Her husband had been a strong man. Strong shoulders, the shoulders of an "ox," had always been her support in her first marriage. And now Monsieur Bucer was asking her to shoulder the burden of Monsieur Calvin's frail health. Monsieur Calvin needed a strong and a patient woman. She did not doubt her ability for patience — but strength? She had health, but was she strong? Could she take on the strong role that a man, on whom life made such great demands, needed?

Monsieur Calvin was reading the Scriptures. The congregation stood as he read as a sign of respect to the reading of the Sacred Word. This was the central part of the service. Idelette was aghast to find how far afield she had permitted her thoughts to wander during divine worship. She had not even heard the short formal prayer for spiritual illumination which preceded the reading of the Scripture.

Idelette followed the Scripture reading in the twelfth chapter of Romans, the first ten verses, in her treasured Bible. At its close the congregation settled back on the benches. The sermon began. As was his custom Monsieur Calvin took nothing to the pulpit but the text. And as he spoke it was obvious that he did not read from any prepared manuscript. He was fortunate to be blessed with a retentive memory and a very find command both of thought and language. He always spoke simply, briefly and directly. And he deliberately avoided any rhetorical ornamentation of speech.

He was always easy to follow or even to transcribe, for

his speech was deliberate, and often slow — for he was frequently handicapped by difficult breathing.

His congregation was well trained. Their pastor had seen to that. "The only proper attitude for hearing a sermon," he would exhort them, "is the attitude of willingness to obey God completely and with no reserve." When his people came to church with that dedication of heart, half of his work was already accomplished.

But in addition to mental attitude, Monsieur Calvin saw to it that his congregation performed certain physical gymnastics to better fit them for the reception of God's Word. In the first place services were held early before any chance of the day's fatigue became apparent. If daylight permitted church would begin as early as six in the morning. On Saturday night a strict curfew was observed. The mind was already started on the road to Sabbath observance. And for Sunday morning, Monsieur Calvin urged little breakfast be eaten. "How can any man profit from the Word when his belly is so full of wine and meat that it takes all his effort just to stay awake?" he would scold.

His sermon of the morning was on the subject, "The Christian Life." And as was his custom his sermon was a running commentary of the passage. . . .

"We have said that the end of regeneration is, that the life of believers may exhibit a symmetry and agreement between the righteousness of God and their obedience; and that thus they may confirm the adoption by which they are accepted as His children. But though the law of God contains in it that newness of life by which His image is restored in us, yet since our tardiness needs much stimulation and assistance, it will be useful to collect from various places of Scripture a rule for the reformation of the life, that they who cordially repent may not be bewildered in their pursuits.

" 'Be not conformed to this world; but be ye transformed by the renewing of your mind, that ye may prove what is that will of God.' This is a very important consideration, that we are consecrated and dedicated to God; that we may not hereafter think, speak, meditate, or do anything but with a view to His glory.

". . . When the Scripture enjoins us to conduct ourselves in such a manner toward men, as in honour to prefer one another, and faithfully to devote our whole attention to the promotion of their advantage, it gives such commands as our heart can by no means receive, without having been previously divested of its natural bias. For we are all so blinded and fascinated with self-love, that every one imagines he has a just right to exalt himself, and to undervalue all others who stand in competition with him. . . . The poor yield to the rich, plebeians to nobles, servants to masters, the illiterate to the learned; but there is no man who does not cherish within him some idea of his own excellence. Thus all men, in flattering themselves, carry, as it were, a kingdom in their own breast: for arrogating to themselves the height of self-gratulation, they pass censure on the understandings and conduct of others.

". . . We must remember, that the talents with which God has favoured us, are not excellences originating from ourselves, but free gifts of God; of which if any are proud, they betray their ingratitude. 'Who maketh thee to differ?' saith Paul . . . On the other hand we are enjoined, whatever gifts of God we perceive in others, to revere and esteem them, so as to honour those in whom they reside. For it would betray great wickedness in us to rob them of that honour which God has given them. Their faults we are taught to overlook, not indeed to encourage them by adulation, but never on account of them to insult those whom we ought to cherish with benevolence and honour.

". . . Let this, then, be our rule for benignity and beneficence — that whatever God has conferred on us, which enables us to assist our neighbor, we are the stewards of it, and must one day render an account of our stewardship; and that the only right dispensation of what has been committed to us, is that which is regulated by the law of love. Thus we shall not always connect the study to promote the advantage of others with a concern for our own private interest, but shall prefer the good of others to our own.

"Pious people should feel tranquility and patience; the same state of mind ought to be extended to all the events to which the present life is exposed. Therefore no man has rightly renounced himself, but he who has wholly resigned himself to the Lord, so as to leave all the parts of his life to be governed by His will. He whose mind is thus composed, whatever may befall him, will neither think himself miserable, nor invidiously complain against God on account of his lot. The great necessity of this disposition will appear, if we consider the numerous accidents to which we are subject. Diseases of various kinds frequently attack us; at one time, the pestilence is raging; at another, we are cruelly harassed with the calamities of war; at another time frost or hail, devouring the hopes of the year, produces sterility, which brings us to penury; a wife, parents, children, or other relatives, are snatched away by death. . . . these are the events, on the occurrence of which, men curse this life, or their natal day, execrate heaven and earth, reproach God, and, as they are eloquent to blaspheme, accuse him of injustice and cruelty. But it behooves a believer, even in these events, to contemplate the clemency and truly paternal goodness of God. Wherefore, if he sees his relatives removed, and his house rendered a solitary place, he must not cease to bless the Lord, but rather have recourse to this reflection: Yet the grace of the Lord, which inhabits my house, will not leave it desolate. . . .

"On the contrary the rule of piety is, that God alone is the arbiter and governor of all events, both prosperous and adverse, and that He does not proceed with inconsiderate impetuosity, but dispenses to us blessing and calamities with the most systematic justice."

The sermon was ended. Idelette followed carefully every phrase of the long liturgical petition of general supplication ending in the Lord's prayer. The children with their light voices joined her in the rich phrases, *"Notre Père qui es aux cieux! Que Ton nom soit sanctifié; que Ton règne vienue; que Ta volonté soit faite sur la terre comme au ciel. . . ."*

They sang together the Apostles' Creed. Charles, his anger forgotten, was singing now in his sweet boy soprano. As the benediction was pronounced, peace engulfed her — the peace and tranquility of which the pastor had spoken. It was as if a bitterness, which she had not known lay within her, had gone. She felt blessed.

5

The evening hours were precious to Idelette. Hers was a personality that thrived on time for solitude and meditation. These were too often crowded out during her busy work day. She longed for an uncluttered mind. Tonight she was especially grateful to be alone with her thoughts and with God.

Idelette was conscientious in this matter of prayer. She had been taught by Pastor Calvin that the principal exercise of faith is prayer, and she was faithful in the matter of family and private devotions. This evening she disciplined her mind to the first step in prayer. Monsieur Calvin had pointed out to his congregation that one "should apply all his faculties and attention to it, and not be distracted, as is commonly the case, with wandering thoughts; nothing being more contrary to a reverence for God than such levity, which indicates a licentious spirit, wholly unrestrained by fear. . . . No man can be so intent on praying, but he may experience many irregular thoughts intruding on him, and either interrupting, or by some oblique digression retarding, the course of his devotions. But here let us consider what an indignity it is, when God admits us to familiar intercourse with Him, to abuse such great condescension by a mixture of things sacred and profane, while our thoughts are not confined to Him by reverential awe; but as if we were conversing with a mean mortal, we quit Him in the midst of our prayer, and make excursions on every side."

Idelette was aware also that prayers seldom were answered instantaneously. As she had heard Monsieur Calvin say, "It is not possible for God to humor us as soon as we have opened our mouths and formed our request. But it is needful that He delay and that He let us languish oftentimes so that we may know what it is to call upon Him sincerely and without pretense."

Idelette also realized that although a Christian must have patience in praying and continue steadfast in prayer that there did on occasion come a time when it became evident that the prayer would not be answered as the petitioner herself wanted. For one's own good God could and did withhold answers that a Christian desired, although in the truest sense of the word the prayer was answered; for none would be so brash as to pray for something which ultimately would be bad for his soul. At moments like this, she had heard Monsieur Calvin say, "But when we are convinced that He must pass by some need, and that the will of God is known to us, then it is no longer a matter of making of Him another request, unless that He may strengthen us in power and in invincible constancy, and that we may make no complaint, or that we may not be carried away by our affections; but that we may go with a ready courage through everything to which He calls us."

In all honesty she had to confess that such a time had come for her. All week she had been praying that God would lead that she would not be the woman to share Monsieur Calvin's life. She had hoped that Monsieur Bucer would come to say that the arrangement was terminated. It was quite evident that her prayer was going to be one that God would answer negatively. She was even ashamed of herself for having prayed so one-sidedly. She should have prayed for God's guidance and kept an open mind. How grateful she was that God was a Father who could understand the feeble motives which drove her away from a new marriage. She was especially comforted by what Monsieur Calvin so often told his flock that "God allured people to

Him. He imitated the pattern we associate with earthly fathers who tell their children 'I will give you a lovely hat; I will buy you a pretty dress' to show us affection for we are little and tenderlets." How much of a "tenderlet" she had been.

As she prayed she was conscious, as always, how much her own family owed its spiritual health to Monsieur Calvin, the pastor of Saint Nicolas. Her own prayer life had been strengthened by his ministry. Even now, as she faced this big decision in her life, ironically much of her thinking was the Christian type of thinking which she would never have known if it had not been for Jean Calvin.

This morning she had been especially rebuked when he had pointed out in his sermon that even though God takes all, how blessed we are if He abides with us. Truly if we have everything but not God, how miserable we are. If, on the other hand, we have nothing but God, how truly blessed we are. "The grace of the Lord, which inhabits my house, will not leave it desolate." God had taken Jean, but He had not Himself departed from her. All day long these words of Monsieur Calvin had been a song in her heart.

Monsieur Calvin had made another statement in the morning's sermon which had been recurring in her mind all day. A true Christian has to consider the rights of others first — not that he should neglect his own, but when there is no religious conflict in honor one must prefer the other. How was it Monsieur Calvin had stated it, "We shall prefer the good of others to our own"?

It was becoming increasingly apparent to Idelette that her main reason for withholding her consent to marriage was one of sentimentality. She would prefer to remain a widow steadfast to the memory of Jean Stordeur. Hers was not a flippant nature, and when love came it came slowly but abided. But if it were true that she should prefer the good of others to her own, she had no good reason to refuse to marry Jean Calvin. No one knew more personally than herself what good the man had done for the religious life of Saint Nicolas. If she could, by her marriage to him, aid him in his work, could she as a Christian in honor not prefer him?

The candle burned low. Idelette was frugal enough not to want to light another. She folded her hands on the round table and bowed her head in them. There was no need to postpone decision any longer. She would say "Yes." And if this marriage, unlike her first, was entered into not with exultation but resignation, Idelette was content. She was doing what she felt to be right.

6

The bans were published for the marriage of Jean Calvin and Idelette Stordeur three Sundays before the wedding day. After Idelette's consent to the marriage had been obtained Monsieur Calvin lost no time in setting the marital machinery in motion. It was a cardinal principle with him than an engagement should not last longer than six weeks.

The first reading of the bans had taken the congregation of the Petite Eglise by surprise. Idelette felt eyes focusing on her where she sat. She could almost read the minds of those about her, "How utterly unworldly Monsieur Calvin is. He would have done so much better to have married that rich Mademoiselle. Her brother is so fond of our pastor and was so anxious to have him in the family. Do you suppose it is true that Monsieur Calvin would not have her because she could not speak French? Now he has saddled himself with a penniless widow and two small children."

Or perhaps they were thinking, "I wonder what happened to make Monsieur Calvin break his engagement to that enchanting Mademoiselle . . . what was her name? But you know, Monsieur Calvin's brother, Antoine, and Claude Feray had it all arranged. Claude told me she was poor but simply fascinating. Monsieur Calvin must have discovered something scandalous about her, or could she have an incurable disease? Monsieur Calvin is so strict about broken betrothals on any other grounds. He certainly found out fast. He was only engaged three days. A widow at least will not be skittish. Idelette Stordeur is a good woman, but what does he see in her?"

Idelette kept her own eyes down while the ripple of shock went through the congregation. She felt Charles twisting and fidgeting on the seat beside her. Only Judith kept her eyes open and smiled enchantingly at everyone, especially at Monsieur Calvin.

Meanwhile Monsieur le Curé ignored the sensation the announcement had made and with complete aplomb went on to deliver a sermon which many considered the best he had preached that year. His days of nervous waiting were over. There was nothing to be upset about now. Monsieur Calvin was betrothed, and that was that.

This formality of the public announcement of the approaching marriage was repeated two more Sundays. Then finally the big day, Tuesday, August 10, 1540, arrived. The congregation of the Pete Eglise was out early. The renowned Monsieur Guillaume Farel was coming from Switzerland to perform the ceremony.

At home Idelette was combing her thick black hair, parting it cleanly in the middle, pulling it straight back and exposing her lovely forehead, accenting by the simplicity of her coiffure her deep oval eyes. Judith, already dressed, looked very sweet. Charles, as usual, waited his turn scuffing his feet on the floor. Idelette fingered her wedding dress. She had made it herself of material which she treasured, since it was some which she had brought with her from the old home in Liege. She had made the sleeves in the puffed mouton style that was so fashionable. The loveliest part of the dress was the stand-up collar which was trimmed with the finest of Brussels lace. She hoped the gown was not too ornate for the wedding dress of a bride of a Reformer. She decided against any jewelry other than the silver belt which accentuated her tiny waist.

Taking a child's hand in each of her own Idelette walked for the last time from her room in her brother's house to the church. They were early, but it was just as well. Monsieur Calvin was always very strict about the punctuality of wedding parties. The sermon which always followed the church's blessing on the wedding couple must never be delayed by a temperamental bride or groom. Monsieur Calvin was even earlier than they. As he watched the little family come in he felt for the first time that pride a man feels as he sees his own.

One could hear a sentimental sigh from the congregation as Jean Calvin took his place beside his chosen ones. Idelette did not raise her eyes. Charles glowered and swung his feet rebelliously. But Judith placed a tiny hand on Monsieur Calvin's sleeve, and when he smiled down at her fluttered her eyelashes at him.

The great Monsieur Farel, whom few in the Petite Eglise had seen before, received the vows. This was a high honor their small church of Saint Nicolas was receiving. The congregation was all fond of Monsieur Calvin. It was difficult, however, for them to realize as he went about quietly ministering to them the magnitude of their pastor on the religious horizon. An occasion like this underlined it. And they were proud of him. Monsieur Farel performed the ceremony with the dignity expected from him.

When it was Idelette's turn to take her solemn vows it seemed to her that Monsieur Farel stressed the passage, "In sickness and in health." All of Monsieur Calvin's friends had made it perfectly clear to her that what they wanted most from her for him was her "comforting care." Her bridegroom himself had even written to this very man who was performing the marriage, "The only beauty, that makes an impression on me, is that, if a wife shows herself gentle, chaste, discreet, domestic, patient, and when the care of her husband is her main aim."

Idelette took her vows steadily, with earnestness. She had known love. Now, in duty, she would marry this great man so often sick, and she would care for him. Yes, she would cherish him "in sickness and in health."

The marriage vows were taken. Monsieur and the new Madame Calvin resumed their places on the bench in front

beside the children. The sermon began. Monsieur Farel
was at his most eloquent best. He was elated by the marriage of his friend. Although himself a bachelor — his rug-
ged health did not demand a helpmate — he was all in
favor of his more delicate friend seeking what solace life
could give him. Carried away by the occasion he was also
at his longest. The August sun beat down on the roof, and
the small church became very hot. Charles squirmed.
Even Monsieur Calvin stirred a little. Judith and Idelette
sat with disciplined stillness.

It was over at last. Jean Calvin had no time for even
a word with his new bride, for when they reached the court-
yard they were surrounded by their many well-wishers.
Claude Feray came forward and took the two children away
with him to Madame Bucer. Kind Elizabeth Bucer had invited a few friends in to a wedding dinner.

As soon as they were able the newlyweds walked together with the other invited guests to the Bucer home in
Thomas Square. The men talked with one another. Idelette
said nothing. She would have thought he had forgotten her
if Monsieur Calvin had not taken her arm to help her around
the rough places in the cobblestone streets.

Today was not just a wedding to the Martin Bucers,
Guillaume Farel, the Pierre Virets, Claude Feray, Florimond
de Raemond, Antoine Calvin and the others. It was an opportunity to visit and to discuss the religious problems of
the day. And as they took their places around the table
the men ate and talked among themselves. Whenever Jean
Calvin looked up to see his new wife she was sitting quietly
listening to the other women. Once while looking at her
he stopped his sentence in mid-air, and fumbled for his
context. Antoine, his brother, laughed.

And thus the day was spent, and when the group finally
broke up, the Calvins were still not alone, for the child
Judith walked between them to their home, and they talked
with her. Claude had wisely already taken an unruly
Charles home. But Judith had begged to remain, and permission had been granted to her.

The house looked warm and beautiful as they entered the yard. All the details of poverty had been erased by the kind darkness. And Claude in a burst of youthful extravagance had lit a candle in each window. He was not in sight when they entered and no doubt his act had insured the absence of the other pensioners and the garrulous housekeeper. Monsieur Calvin was grateful. Idelette turned toward him, and for the first time that day he caught her eyes. Even now she dropped her lashes quickly. "I shall put Judith to bed, and shall be with you presently."

He stooped down to the child's level, "Good-night, my daughter," he said holding out his hand.

Judith put her own tiny hand into his, and dropped a curtsy, "Good-night, my father." And then seeing his kind face so close to her own, she put her arms about his neck and kissed him.

Reluctantly the little girl went with Idelette. Jean Calvin waited a moment before he followed them. He could hear their soft voices as he passed the child's tiny room. He opened the door to Claude's room. Claude and the boy were both asleep. He placed a light covering over them. His heart went out to this child who was now his son. Charles Stordeur had not been responsive to him. But Claude had made a friend. "No one," thought Monsieur Calvin, "can resist the sweetness of Claude Feray." He hoped things would work out. Monsieur Bucer had been so sure this was the match God intended for him. He had pointed out Idelette's piety, sweetness and beauty. And he, himself, whenever he thought of the Widow Stordeur, had been haunted by thoughts which would do a marriage no harm.

Providence had led. So be it. He softly closed the door, entered his own bedroom and prepared for bed. As he waited for Idelette he sat in his favorite chair by the window overlooking the Petite Eglise, the church of his heart. But he found it difficult to sit. This perturbation of spirit was new to him, and he felt the need for calmness. He picked up the Bible at his elbow on the wide window sill and started to read Scripture passages on the subject of marriage. And thus he waited for Idelette.

Idelette tucked the covers in around her little girl. Judith's face was flushed. The excitement of the wedding had brought unusual color to her sallow cheeks. It was becoming to her . . . Not usually demonstrative, tonight Idelette bent down and kissed her daughter good-night, and with her usual docility Judith responded.

Idelette would have liked to have held Charles, too, in her arms, but her son was sleeping in Claude Feray's room. She dared not even tiptoe in as she passed. Charles had been rude at the wedding, sulking in his handsome tempestuous way. It was only Claude who had kept the situation under control and the other guests from noticing. Or perhaps they had in kindness only pretended not to see. If only Charles could feel for Monsieur Calvin what he so spontaneously felt for Claude.

She frowned as she walked slowly down the hall. When she reached the threshold of her own room, she hesitated, and in a moment of timidity found herself hurrying back to Judith's room. The child already slept. In the darkness Idelette undressed and slipped into her nightrobe. She took down her thick black hair, and picking up the child's brush, stroked her own hair vigorously. Judith stirred, and hastily Idelette laid down the brush. What was wrong with her to act so childishly, Idelette prodded herself. She was ashamed at her own behavior. She straightened her shoulders, threw back her head, and without further delay walked directly to the room that would be hers and Monsieur Calvin's.

When Jean Calvin saw her, her tiny oval face was held high, and her lovely black hair spilled about her shoulders. He closed his Bible and firmly replaced it on the sill. Then he held out his arms toward her. And as she walked steadily to him he said very softly, "I have been reading the fifth chapter of Proverbs. I have found, my dear, one command which I shall not find hard to keep, 'Rejoice with the wife of thy youth.'"

7

The household to which Jean Calvin brought his bride consisted of the teacher, Claude Feray, the favorite pensioner of Jean Calvin, and the two pupils he brought with him, Louis and Charles Malheibe. For a time Monsieur Calvin had kept his housekeeper and her son under the mistaken notion that it would make Idelette's work easier. But after the dour woman became more and more difficult to bear her final departure over an imaginary slight she had received from the hands of Antoine Calvin was greeted with no sorrow. Monsieur Calvin made no effort to persuade her to return, as he had done on previous occasions; and the life settled down to a happy routine.

Eynard Pichon and Nicolas Parent had moved out to make room for Idelette and her children; but they were frequent visitors. Monsieur Calvin had once described Nicolas as all "fire and flames." His personality was a guarantee against any dullness. Antoine Calvin who lived more often than not with his brother was now staying with their step-sister, Marie Calvin, who had joined the family — leaving her home in Picardy to throw in her lot with them. There was a warm family bond among the three Calvins. It was always difficult to say whether Jean's brother and sister were living under Jean Calvin's roof or merely frequent overnight guests.

The assignment of rooms in the pension now run by

Idelette gave the most comfortable room in the house to Claude's pupils, who paid very well. This room was large and sunny and faced the street. Claude, who paid little for his board and room, insisted that young Charles permanently share his bedroom and thus give the married couple some measure of privacy — for there was a tiny room, scarcely more than a cupboard, which sufficed for little Judith.

Jean and Idelette's bedroom was small, but its windows overlooked the tiny enclosed churchyard, and Idelette liked it best of all her rooms. It looked spacious for it had little furniture, one chest of drawers, Monsieur Calvin's favorite chair and a large bed. This bed itself was a luxury for Idelette. During her first marriage Idelette's husband had for many years been a refugee and they had of necessity led a hand-to-mouth existence, so that they had never indulged in anything other than the pallets used by the poor.

Adjoining this bedroom was Jean Calvin's study. Its only ornamentation was its priceless library. It contained a chair, a desk, and a step-ladder on which to climb to reach the books which filled the bookcases to the ceiling.

With care and thrift, Idelette was able to make the budget stretch for the essentials. But there were always so many needy people who found their way to Monsieur Calvin's door. It seemed impossible for him to turn any away unaided. Many a time a valuable book would disappear from the bookshelf in Calvin's study. Idelette seeing the gap would realize it had been sold in order to feed some hungry supplicant. Idelette, in good conscience, under such conditions could not indulge herself in any frivolities.

Her furniture remained as miscellaneous as when she had arrived; the only feminine whim she allowed herself was flowers. Before her own began to bloom in her tiny yard, she hoarded her sous, and when she felt she had been niggardly enough with the household accounts she would reward herself with a bouquet from the flower market. More often nosegays were brought to her by the cheerful rich young boarders, Charles and Louis. Occasionally, in an ecstasy of extravagance, Claude Feray would shower her with an armful of her favorite posies. For this he was always roundly scolded.

Once, Monsieur Calvin bought some daffodils; but he forgot to give them to her. And it was only when he was replacing one of his priceless books on the shelf that he found the forgotten blossoms squashed under a stack of them. He had laughed as he handed them belatedly to her, "I am afraid I am too old to learn. I shall have to leave gallantry to the gallants."

It was a happy home. The students were good to the children and fond of Idelette. Charles Stordeur adored the young teacher Claude Feray, and under his gentle hand, responded by an occasional return to his original sweet disposition. Judith, as usual, was content anywhere. Claude, especially, did everything to make the new bride happy. It was his way of showing how deep his affection was for the man whose intellect and life he admired so tremendously. And Jean Calvin glowed in his newfound happiness. He was delighted with the smooth running of his household. It was a joy to bring friends to his home presided over by the wife of whom he was growing so proud.

A pleasure the new bridegroom had not anticipated was the joy of sharing his experiences, his thoughts, even his problems. In the past, Jean Calvin had been richly blessed with a few close friends in whom he had always confided with abandon. But this opportunity to reveal his thoughts and unload his burdens at will with another who was always on hand brought a deep measure of contentment.

Then, too, Jean Calvin loved to revel in the beauty of his wife. His practical friend, Guillaume Farel, had said of Idelette that she was honest and very beautiful. Jean had never doubted her honesty, but it was only with the passing of the days that he began truly to see the beauty of his wife. She had an inner tranquility which was reflected in her eyes, in her smooth, unlined oval face. It was seen even in her walk, or the way she turned her head or moved her hands. He had at first found this quietness disturbing. Now he could read the secret of her stillness. Idelette had achieved an inner poise which permeated every move she made.

Tonight when sleep eluded Jean, he lay beside the sleeping Idelette and reviewed her past life — the past which had produced this woman he was growing to love. She had lived a full lifetime of sorrow. God grant her days with him be easier ones. Her girlhood in Liege, Belgium, had not been carefree. Her beloved father, an Anabaptist, had been convicted of heresy, banished from home — his goods confiscated. Her husband's three brothers, Libert, Gerard and Denis Stordeur, had been made to walk through Liege in nightshirts with ropes around their necks. She and her husband Jean Stordeur had fled for their lives more than once for conscience' sake. They had suffered gallantly — even if misguidedly — from his own hands. For he had been instrumental in the banishment of the Stordeur family from Geneva for their heretical Anabaptist beliefs.

God led them, even as He had led himself to Strasbourg; and here, in that city of peace, ruled by the kind and tolerant mayor, Jacob Sturm, it had been finally he, Jean Calvin, who had been the chosen instrument of the Almighty to lead Jean Stordeur to the light. This new convert had been a zealot for any cause he was convinced to be right. He had become a good friend and faithful supporter of Calvin. How strange to remember how little he, Jean Calvin, had noticed the young wife in those early days — the young wife who always stayed in the background. It was not until the terrible night of Jean Stordeur's death of the plague that he had ever really noticed Madame Stordeur. He smiled as he recalled how uneasy she had made him.

He looked down at the face that was already becoming sweetly familiar to him. The long lashes left smudgy shadows. Idelette's soft even breathing told him she was asleep. He leaned over and kissed her. She stirred but did not waken. He sank back against the hard bed feeling a trifle foolish. He smiled ruefully. It was a wonderful feeling to fall in love with one's wife. "In the beginning," he repeated to himself, "God created male and female, male and female created He them." Martin Bucer was right. Marriage was good. The great man was happy.

8

Jean Calvin was not the only person made happy by his marriage. His inner circle of friends caught the contagion of his joy. Martin Bucer smugly took his full share of credit for the accomplished feat. His good wife, Elizabeth, grew weary of hearing the story of his successful wooing of Idelette. But she wisely refrained from ever indicating that it was actually she who had dropped the seed of the attractive widow into Martin's romantic bosom. Cheerfully, she let him reap where he had not sown.

Elizabeth Bucer, herself, was happy and relieved. Unlike her optimistic spouse, her own feelings had fallen somewhat short of complete confidence in the outcome of the marriage. She had no doubt that the match was a good one. Ever since Idelette had arrived in Strasbourg, Elizabeth had liked her. They had never become intimate, for Idelette was a woman who kept much to herself. But the gallantly uncomplaining way Idelette went through life aroused in Elizabeth a godly envy.

Elizabeth realized that she, by comparison, had led a sheltered life. Martin, himself, robust in health, cheerful in disposition, had suited her ideally. They had been blessed with five happy, healthy children. Her life had not known any great calamity. She wondered, as all do who have never really suffered, how she herself would have met the successive tragedies Idelette had known. Elizabeth also admired a trait of Idelette which was quite foreign to her own nature — her quietness. Elizabeth, herself, was loquacious, and though careful not to be malicious, enjoyed the soft gossip which most church women enjoy among themselves.

Elizabeth's concern over the outcome of the marriage lay not with the person of Idelette, but rather the character of Jean Calvin. He was a man who was ever striving for perfection — so unlike her good Martin who overlooked a great deal. Also Jean Calvin was extremely sensitive and avoided whenever possible any wrangling — the sort that her own husband thrived upon. Elizabeth admired Jean Calvin greatly; but at the same time her practical spirit made her realize these characteristics of his could present marital obstacles. In all honesty she doubted if she herself could have met the challenge of the post of Madame Calvin.

Her hope for the success of the marriage lay in the character of Idelette. And she, too, was happy her hope was being fulfilled. She had felt that Idelette, a widow, would enter into the arrangement with no dewy-eyed naiveté, and she was being proven right. It always irritated Elizabeth when she heard people say that the success of a marriage was insured only if each party contributed equally to its workings. Since the male member of the marriage must be out in the world earning a livelihood and a woman's whole work was her marriage, it had always been Elizabeth's position that the logic of the situation demanded a greater responsibility from the wife. This positive thinking had worked well and happily in her adjustments with Martin. And she sensed with a canniness which was a part of her personality that Idelette shared her viewpoint.

Jean Calvin's brother, Antoine, was another who was made happy by his brother's new home life. Idelette would never have been his choice. He preferred more vivacity and personality in a woman. Idelette always seemed shadowy to him. The women in his own family were quite different. His step-sister, Marie, was cute and pert. Give him more sauce in his wife; but he was not a student, and he was quick to realize that Idelette was a scholar's choice. Besides, after his own choice for a sister-in-law had turned out so disastrously, he was content with Idelette.

Jean Calvin's step-sister Marie liked Idelette. She found her to be a woman's woman — one who never offered competition. Marie liked the role that was hers in her gifted brother's life. She enjoyed being the sister of a noted man. She was bright and would frequently enter into the discussions with the men. Her remarks were always heard with deference because of her brother. Marie was quite aware that her brother could have married an erudite woman who would have displaced her. She was relieved by her brother's choice. She could afford to like Idelette.

What Marie Calvin did not realize was that Idelette was her equal in theological acumen. Marie did not know that after the guests left the silent Idelette would speak with Jean and often the profound discussions were continued in private by them. Jean Calvin was aware that there were few who appreciated this facet of Idelette's personality. It was as if his wife preferred to stay in the shadows. She was like a woman of the Orient, who veiled herself on the streets, and revealed herself fully only to the man who was her own. She wanted no acclaim from others. It became increasingly evident to Jean Calvin that she sought only to please God and him.

In all his close relationships with others, and his many deep friendships, Jean Calvin had never known such effacement. He, who was accustomed to defer to others, found in her an eager and intelligent disciple. He loved to teach her and it warmed his heart to realize that he and Idelette possessed a rare gift, the communion of the mind.

9

Judith opened her eyes and looked around her new bedroom. By lying on one side she could see out her tiny window. There on a chimney of an adjoining house a stork had built its nest. Claude had told her the same stork family had been coming back in the spring from Africa to their home on the chimney top for as long as he had lived there. Storks liked human beings and wanted to live near them. Every year he had watched the storks add to the old nest. Now the pile of sticks on which the nest perched was several feet high. It looked like a platform.

Only yesterday Judith had noticed little wobbly heads peeking up over the edge. All the tiny mouths were wide open. They made no noise for they were voiceless. They did not need to cry, for the patient mother bird flew silently down to the ground and back up again with a steady supply of food.

This was the first time Judith had ever had a room to herself. Before, she and Charles and her mother had shared the same room. It made her feel a young lady to have this privacy. Only at night she sometimes wished she were not quite so old, for it would have felt comforting to snuggle up to someone in the darkness.

Charles opened her door and came in. "How many little storks are there?"

"I don't know."

"Silly. You never know anything. Why don't you count them?"

"I can only count to ten."

"Ha!" Judith's brother was scornful. "That would be far enough. Who ever heard of a stork having as many as ten babies in one nest?" He swung one leg over the window sill, and for her benefit counted on his fingers. "Four. She only has four babies. Judith, you will watch carefully, won't you? Uncle Claude says one day they'll learn to fly. I want to see the mother stork teach them. You will call me when it happens, won't you? I wish I could fly."

"People don't fly," Judith said matter-of-factly.

"Angels do."

"But you must die to be an angel."

"Then I shall die. But I must learn to fly." Charles swayed out the window ledge, clinging only with his knees, and flapped his arms. Claude Feray, in his night shirt, blond hair tousled, came in and grabbed the young demonstrator.

"Patience, young man. Let the mother stork teach the babies. You are no substitute teacher. Besides, let babies enjoy their nests as long as they can. Stork mothers are the very best. They take especially good care of their young. You may be sure that as soon as she knows it is safe the mother will stir up the nest and push the fledglings out."

"Oh, no!" Judith was distressed.

"Then they can fly to the sun," Charles exulted.

"I wish they would always stay in the nest."

Claude sat down beside Judith on the edge of the bed. "If they stayed where they are they would grow bigger, and bigger, and bigger, and lazier, and lazier, and lazier. At the right time, their mother, who is wiser than they, will teach them to fly. Wait and see."

Claude enjoyed his mornings with the children. He hoped someday he would have children of his own, and that they would be a little like these two of Madame Idelette Calvin. He had not at first, actually, anticipated the marriage of his friend, — Jean Calvin. In spite of the difference in their ages his affection for the older man had been deep, analagous to that close friendship of Jonathan and David, surpassing, he had felt, the love of women. But Idelette Calvin and her little family had not estranged him from Jean Calvin, or in any way broken the bonds of the friendship he cherished. It was as if all their hearts had stretched a little to take each other in.

10

It never entered Jean Calvin's mind to wonder if his wife loved him. As long as she discharged her wifely duties faithfully he asked no more. Marriage, after all, was ordained of God for two reasons: the bearing of offspring and as a remedy against incontinence. In his own case his ill health had been an added persuasive. Honesty compelled him to realize that he was of value to the cause of the Reformation which was so dear to his heart, and since the Divine Creator had not blessed him with the gift of robust health, it was all the more his duty to safeguard and nurture his limited strength. A wife, his friends had repeatedly told him, could take from his shoulders many of the petty worries that sapped his meager supply of health. When he had become convinced that their arguments were reasonable, he had acted.

He had not counted on more than a mutual affection and esteem to make the marriage a success. This deep passion he felt for his beautiful bride was totally unexpected, but nevertheless welcome. Jean Calvin counted it as another evidence of a gracious gift from a benevolent God.

Although he was aware as the days passed of his own growing love for his wife, he did not realize the emotional upheaval that was going on in the woman who cooked his meals, cared for his household, and made life comfortable for him. Idelette's serenity of manner disguised successfully, even from him, the tumult she was experiencing in her new relationship. Idelette, herself, had entered into this marriage for reasons of duty. She had not expected to fall in love. She had been so certain the feeling she had known for Jean Stordeur could never be duplicated. She had been so sure, too, that Monsieur Calvin's attitude toward her would be unsentimental. It was, therefore, most disturbing to her peace of mind to have it otherwise. Idelette's first husband had been uneloquent, a man not given to conversation especially about any of the deeper emotions. Monsieur Calvin, always eloquent, outdid himself when declaring his love for her. His words of endearment were like a psalm. They would flow over her, and she found herself caught up in the tide of his devotion.

She was uneasy about the situation and her role in this new marriage. She tried to avoid any occasion for self-analyzation by submerging any thought in the many new problems which arose in the new home. She had much to think about. Charles, although better, still had his black moods. He was becoming steadily worse in his relationship to her. One day he had been behaving unbearably rudely, when Jean Calvin entered the room.

"Never," he had thundered at the boy, "never let me hear you use that tone of voice to your mother again."

Idelette was afraid the child would answer back. Charles had pulled himself up to his full height and had stared defiantly at his step-father. But seeing those indignant flashing eyes fixed upon him, he had crumpled into the little boy he really was, and had left the room in tears. Idelette had started to follow him.

"Stay here, Idelette."

Idelette started to remonstrate. Then didn't.

"His tears are not those of penitence, but impotent rage. Let him weep. You spoil the lad." Jean Calvin had been angry. It was the first rebuke he had ever directed at her. It hurt. But she knew her husband was right. After all this was one of the primary reasons she had desired a remarriage for herself — a firmer hand for the boy. She spoke as if to herself, "I know I am indulgent where he is concerned. I cannot bear to punish him. He looks so like his father. . . ."

Jean Calvin was disturbed by her answer. He realized it was illogical to react this way, for from the first Idelette had appealed to him because of her tender care and affection for Jean Stordeur, his friend. Why then, this spontaneous resentment at every mention of his name? He was still angry when he chided her again, "If he looks so like the good Jean Stordeur, then you must teach him to act like him, or I shall."

Idelette's back stiffened. She resented this usurpation of the discipline of her son. But was it usurpation? Had not her marriage given Jean Calvin this right? Her answer when it came was meek, "I shall endeavor to do so."

Thereafter Idelette was firmer with the boy; but he continued to misbehave. Only when he saw the shadow of his step-father he simulated an unwilling obedience. And on the occasions when Claude had the time to play with him, he brightened into his old lovable self.

But Charles and his problems of adjustment were finally pushed into the background by her own more immediate preoccupation with her own marital relationship. She had been avoiding any issues, behaving like a school girl, and it was time she faced up to the fact. She knew, now, that the presence or absence of Jean Calvin in a crowded room made that room full or empty. She found herself making silly excuses to sew or mend quietly while he worked. Even when her husband took Judith on his lap to tell her Bible stories, she found herself sitting beside the two of them, wanting to be a part of them. In the forthright manner she handled problems she decided it was time to get alone by herself and think this thing through.

Her bedroom was the only room in the house where she could seclude herself with any hope for privacy. She sat in Jean Calvin's chair and deliberately prodded her mind to reverie. She thought of the first time she had ever seen Jean Calvin in the pulpit. She remembered the night Jean Stordeur had died. She analyzed each scene as she made herself focus upon it. The summation of her study could have only one answer. No longer was her feeling for Jean Calvin that of a practical nature. She had known love before; she was not so stupid that she did not realize it had come again. And intuitively, she realized that this was a secret which was not hers to keep. It must be shared with one other.

Idelette knocked on the door of the study. Monsieur Calvin was engrossed in manuscripts. His back was stooped. His face was smudged with the dust of the ages. His fingers were inky. His eyes looked up impatiently at the interruption. "Yes?" When she did not answer, but stood in the doorway looking steadily at him, he asked impatiently, "Is anything wrong?"

"No, nothing is wrong. But you look so grim. Please wave your wand for me."

Jean Calvin smiled at the biblical allusion. He knew his wife well enough to realize only something important would have kept her standing in the doorway. His impatience vanished. "Enter, Queen Esther. You may have five minutes!"

Idelette smiled at his jest. "I shall need only one."

She was beside his desk now, resting one hand upon it, and looking down at him. Her almond eyes were softer than he had ever seen them.

"I love you, my husband. It has been a revelation to me, and I wanted to waste no time in sharing my news with you. See, I have taken less than my minute!" True to her word, she turned to leave. He reached the door before her, blocked her passage and swept her into his arms.

11

It was six weeks after the wedding when Jean Calvin took suddenly ill. He had high fever, severe headaches, incessant vomiting, and purging. He became so weak that it was necessary for Idelette and Claude to take turns watching by his bedside. One day Jean noticed the absence of his wife. Claude had to give him the bad news that Idelette also had caught the disease.

Elizabeth Bucer came over every day to help Claude with the nursing duties. She found Monsieur Calvin a very impatient invalid. In spite of severe chills which persisted, he insisted on protesting he was better in order to insure her presence with Idelette. His wife was too ill to make any protestations. She lay in Judith's room too weak to care. As a further complication she had developed a deep cough. Elizabeth became worried. She confided in her husband that Jean Calvin would recover. She feared for Idelette.

The doctor prescribed blood-letting, poultices on the congested chest, and pills to reduce the fever. Idelette showed no improvement. She grew steadily weaker. Jean Calvin who was now well enough to be out of bed grew concerned. As he sat by his sick wife he knew a new emotion — fear for a loved one. The good-hearted Elizabeth did little to lift his spirits. Unintentionally her own attempt to console him only made him realize that she too shared his worry. Idelette was so weak she could not lift her head un-aided from her pillow.

How vulnerable love makes one, thought Jean Calvin, who had himself stoically survived countless bouts with in-fluenza. He prayed with lips still cracked from fever, "Not Idelette, dear God, please not yet, not yet."

There was no immediate answer to his prayer, but after several weeks Idelette rallied and showed some improve-ment. In time she was able to be up and about again, only her nagging cough lingered with her.

Jean Calvin took this experience as one from the chastening hand of God, who sends the bitter with the sweet. In remorse he wrote intimately confiding in his friend Guillaume Farel, "God sent the illness in order to temper our joy in that it would not exceed all bounds."

The honeymoon was over.

12

It was in March, 1541, that plague broke out again in Strasbourg. Jean Calvin was away in the German city of Ratisbon attending the Fourth Diet. News trickled through slowly to the worried men away from home. Idelette and the children, Jean learned, had left the pension to move in with her brother and family. Antoine and Marie had found temporary lodging in a small town outside the infected plague area.

In the midst of important theological debates of world shaking moment Jean Calvin's heart had the added burden of concern for his own. His worry was augmented a hundredfold by the enforced geographical separation. What news he continued to receive was all bad. The hardest blow was to learn that Claude Feray had died. Claude had shown such promise. He had been one of the choicest of all his young friends. It was hard to accept the fact that the splendid intellect he had shown would not reach fruition on this earth.

Jean Calvin heard also that the home where Idelette had sought a haven was in mourning. Charles and Antoinette de Bure had lost their son. What of Idelette herself? Had she escaped? She had been so frail when he left, never having completely recovered from her severe bout with the fever.

Like the scourge it was, as suddenly as it had appeared

the Black Death swept past. People began to return to their homes in Strasbourg, the city of the dead. But it was not until June that Jean Calvin was able to ask conscientiously to be released from his duties in Ratisbon.

Idelette, when she saw her husband again, had been distressed by the change in him. He who had always been too thin was now gaunt. He, in turn, relieved that she was alive was gravely concerned for she seemed scarcely more than a whisper of herself. They clung together in their moment of reunion made tragic by their shared grief over their many beloved dead.

As the Calvins left the home of Idelette's bereaved brother to return to their own pension it was a hard homecoming. Claude was so sadly missed. Young Charles Stordeur was inconsolable. He refused to sleep in his own bedroom. Idelette ached over her son, but she was at a loss as to how much she should indulge his sorrow. Realizing how full of memories the room was to the boy, it was Jean — in one of his infrequent family decisions — who told Idelette to let Judith and the boy exchange bedrooms.

To this new tiny room Charles would slink away at every opportunity. He was no longer boisterous and rude. Instead he had withdrawn completely to himself. But even in her sorrow and worry over him Idelette could not help being grateful that he was alive. She had her son. Her poor brother and Antoinette! It was a rude shock, therefore, one evening to have her husband suggest they let the boy return to visit his uncle and aunt.

"It would help them both, I am sure, my dear wife. Your brother grieves so much for the child that died. It would help Charles. He needs to be taken away from this environment where everything reminds him of Claude."

"It would take him from me."

"And from me. But we must think first of our duty to Charles. The boy has sustained a bludgeoning series of deaths. His beloved father and now Claude. Even you are dead to him, estranged he feels because of your marriage.

I have tried, but I cannot reach him. He replies dutifully but his heart is far from me."

"Jean, I am sorry. I had hoped so much that you two. . . ."

"I know. In time perhaps, Idelette. In this moment of crisis I cannot help him. Even you, whom he loves with deep devotion, are not the best suited to help. If you value my judgment you will release him from this house of sorrow, and let him repair himself in another emotional climate. In the De Bure home he will feel needed. He will be the comforter and the comforted. A tender plant is easily destroyed in a deluge. For his sake indulge him in a short visit?"

Charles went with his mother's blessing. The days of his visit became weeks and the weeks months. It became increasingly evident to Idelette that her son preferred to stay in the home of her brother. This preference was harder to bear than the loss of death. But not one to brood Idelette busied herself with daily tasks. She spent more time than ever visiting the aged in the congregation of the Petite Eglise. Death would find her in the bereaved home giving what comfort she could. No one — not even Jean — knew from her calm face that she found solace for her own sorrow in the words of comfort which her husband gave those who had lost their own.

"We defraud God of His right if we do not permit Him power of life and death."

Jean Calvin always felt that the saddest of funerals was not the one where grief was evident, but rather where it was absent. Actually one's grief was proportionate to one's gift. If one had been blessed by a loving child, an affectionate husband, when such an one was taken the sorrow would be great. If, however, the child had been unloving or the husband had been wicked the grief would be less. One may learn the difficult lesson of rejoicing in bereavement if one contemplated the richness of years which have been given, and contemplated the thought of reunion hereafter — this was the substance of his comfort. As Job put it, "The Lord *hath given*, the Lord hath taken, blessed be the name of the Lord."

Jean Calvin wrote many letters of consolation during these tragic days — letters which were treasured by their recipients. The father of the Richeburg boy — who had been a pensioner at one time with Jean Calvin — received a letter of condolence when his promising lad died of the plague. The great Reformer wrote to him with tenderness, "He is as one, who, having set sail upon the stormy ocean, is summoned back into port before he reached the open sea. Nor have I wished thee not to grieve. We do not learn a philosophy in the school of Christ which would have us suppress all those feelings which God has given us and turn men into stones. All that we have said is only to this end, to persuade thee to set a term to thy grief, and to assuage it; that when thou pourest out thy heart in tears, as nature and fatherly love dictate, thou mayest not altogether resign thyself to grief."

There were few homes in Strasbourg that did not need consolation. The homes of the tanners, the brewers, the printers, the manufacturers of metal and paper goods, the farmers who raised the famous Strasbourg geese — all had been touched by the angel of death. With his firm and confident message — the love of God which must never be doubted — Jean Calvin quietly went his way ministering to the flock of Saint Nicolas, to the people of his own Petite Eglise.

13

August came and went. The Calvins had been married a year now. Monsieur Calvin had settled down to a comfortable domesticity. He took his wife for granted. He envisaged years of happy work in Strasbourg. His writing was going well. He was complacent. And then the letter came.

It was the first of many informing him that Geneva, the city from which he had been driven, was seeking his return. They wanted him once more to become the ruler of the city. There seemed to be for him no "ease in Zion." The very suggestion that he return to that difficult place made his knees turn to water. Not combative by disposition he shuddered at the memories of all that he and his friend Guillaume Farel had undergone at the hands of that Protestant city.

At his last preaching service in Geneva members of the congregation had interrupted his message with drawn swords. It was only the interposition of a shield composed of the bodies of his friends that had prevented bloodshed at the steps of the altar. How galling it had been when the governing body, the Council of Two Hundred, had met and given him three days to be out of the city.

The peace of Strasbourg, and now again this. Surely God could not, would not. . . . It was while away from Idelette at the Council of Worms that the first official request to return was handed him by letter. Months dragged by, busy months for Pastor Calvin who tried to push the weighty Geneva call into a corner of his mind. But his friends would not permit this delay. They kept writing urging him to take up the great work. How differently each argued, how individualistically.

The gentle Pierre Viret wrote pointing out the therapeutic value of Switzerland's mountain air and good climate. Jean Calvin replied, not without humor, "I read that passage of your letter, certainly not without a smile, where you show so much concern about my health, and recommend Geneva on that ground. . . . It would have been far preferable to perish once for all than to be tormented again in that place of torture."

The fiery Guillaume Farel blasted him periodically with his importunate thunderings, "Are you waiting for the stones to cry out? If you had been as slow to leave, when we were ordered out of the city, as you are slow to return despite all pleas, things would not have reached their present pass."

His back against the wall, Jean Calvin replied, "The thunderbolts which you so strangely hurl at me, for what reasons I know not, have filled me with the greatest terror and dismay. You know that I have dreaded this summons, but that I have not been dead to it. Then why attack me with such violence as almost to disrupt our friendship?"

Jean Calvin was having severe stomach spasms again. His own inclinations were all for staying in Strasbourg. He wrote the Pastors of Zurich who were also urging his return, "Were I, therefore, to give way to my own feelings, I would rather go beyond the sea than return thither." But he could not escape the army of arguments which cut directly across his own wishes — he was the man of the hour, the man Geneva needed. He capitulated to God's voice. It was to Guillaume Farel he wrote, "I yield my soul chained and bound unto obedience to God."

Idelette had not been deaf to the anguish of soul she knew her husband was undergoing; but she was wise enough to realize that this was his own private Gethsemane. She did not know what his final answer would be, and the night he told her she had asked calmly, "You want to go?"

"No."

"You feel you must go?"

"Yes."

It was that simple. The matter was decided. And in September, 1541, Monsieur Jean Calvin returned to Geneva. He went alone; but as soon as he was able to find lodgings for her and the children he sent for Idelette.

This move to Geneva was presenting Idelette with her own private Gethsemane. For when it came time to pack and leave, Charles begged to remain in Strasbourg with his uncle. Heartbroken, Idelette wrote to Jean for his advice. But this was one decision Jean insisted that Idelette make alone. He refused to command the boy to come. Eventually Idelette yielded to the boy's request and promised to let him stay the winter. It was not too long a time to be apart. And like all big decisions which turn on small ones, it was just as well she did not know that by deciding in this manner, she was giving away to her brother the son of her heart.

14

The Geneva to which Idelette came had about 15,000 inhabitants. From 1549 to 1559 the population was augmented by 5,000 newcomers. Most of these were refugees from France, England, Spain and Italy who wanted to escape from the hand of Rome and live in the new City of God that Jean Calvin was striving to establish in Geneva.

The French historian, Michelte, wrote of this city, "This elite of France, with an elite of Italy, founded the real Geneva. . . . This astonishing asylum lasted by its moral force. No territory, no army: the city of the mind, built by Stoicism on the rock of 'predestination.'"

The citizens of Strasbourg, when Jean Calvin left, voted to retain him as a citizen and continue giving him his stipend. This latter generous gesture Jean Calvin refused; but the honor of citizenship he retained. And for the remainder of his life he remained a citizen of Strasbourg. He ruled Geneva, but he was always an immigrant.

The city of Geneva, not to be outdone in generosity by the citizens of Strasbourg, gave many generous personal gifts to the Jean Calvins. Monsieur Calvin was presented with a new robe. They remained alert to his material needs. Although Monsieur Calvin, even in Geneva, had to resort to selling his library in order to provide for the necessities of life, the occasions were not so frequent as in Strasbourg. The Council Minutes record for posterity the fact that it had been noticed that Monsieur Calvin's coat was wearing threadbare, and he was forthwith voted money to purchase a broadcloth coat.

But by far the loveliest gift the Genevans presented to the Calvins was a place of their own in which to live. The new home on Canon St. was most comfortable and it was a private home. The pension days were over. The house had been furnished for the Calvins — not extravagantly but comfortably. It even had a small garden. And set as it was high on a hill it had the precious addition of a view of the lake around which the thriving Swiss metropolis sprawled.

There were also many practical advantages to this new location. The community fountain from which the Calvins drew water was only a short distance away at the end of Canon St. They were also within easy walking distance of the beautiful and commanding church of St. Pierre, where Monsieur Calvin spent most of his waking hours.

Although Idelette no longer had paying boarders, since the house was large Antoine and Marie Calvin stayed under the Jean Calvin roof. Idelette was fond of her brother-and sister-in-law. She was drawn to them mostly because they, too, shared a deep affection for Jean Calvin. And Idelette realized that they brought a liveliness into the home which her more sedate nature was unable to provide. Laughter was good for the soul. And it was especially pleasant, with as much entertaining as she had to do in Geneva, to feel that the problem of gracious hospitality could always be left safely to these younger siblings of her husband. Idelette herself was happier providing for the guests' material comforts. Light conversation was not one of her gifts.

One of the happiest relationships which developed in Geneva for Idelette was her friendship with Madame Pierre Viret. Pierre Viret had promised to be Jean's assistant in Geneva for six months in the new work which he had helped to persuade Calvin to undertake, and the two families were thrown constantly together. Idelette had come, since her illness in Strasbourg, to depend on the strong and good Elizabeth Bucer. Her absence in Geneva was compensated for in part by this new friend. Madame Viret was taking a place of her own in Idelette's small coterie of personal friends.

Life in Geneva could never be dull, especially when the bachelor minister Guillaume Farel was in town. The Calvin home was his. Idelette, the observer of life, did not miss the fact that his presence always made the vivacious Marie Calvin exert every French charm which she possessed. But the little sister had found an impregnable target in the much scarred bachelor, Guillaume Farel. Marie was no dreamer, and she wasted no time pouting. It was not long before she found a more vulnerable bachelor, Monsieur Costan of Geneva, and settled down with him in 'a house of her own.

Antoine Calvin also soon left the Jean Calvin household for one of his own. He met an attractive Genevan girl and married and moved to the country. It sometimes seemed as if he had never gone, for Antoine and Ann continued to make the Calvin home their city headquarters. But for the greater part of the time, and for the first time since their marriage, the Jean Calvins were alone at last.

15

It was, Idelette found, not always easy to be married to a great man. Sometimes she felt excluded living on the fringes of her husband's life. His days were full with church problems and governmental details. She in turn found herself the official hostess of Geneva for all who passed through. The Council had even enlarged Jean's salary to five hundred florins a year. The extra allotment of twelve measures of corn enabled Idelette to bake more than twenty loaves of bread a week. This compensated to some degree for the drain on the budget, but the encroachment on priceless time of the heavy entertaining could not be repaid.

Somewhere during the busy day her husband had to find time for his voluminous correspondence. People everywhere wrote to him for advice and he was always punctual with his answers. No one was neglected, from the Duchess of Ferrara, daughter of the late King of France, to the humble cobbler in Strasbourg, who had to hire an amanuensis.

Jean Calvin complained pathetically to a close friend, "I have not time to look out of my house at the blessed sun, and if things continue thus I shall forget what sort of appearance it has. When I have settled my usual business, I have so many letters to write, so many questions to answer, that many a night is spent without any offering of sleep being brought to nature."

His schedule for a typical week in Geneva was: Preach every day in each alternate week. Teach theology three days a week. Attend weekly meetings of the Consistory.

Read the Scriptures once a week in the congregation. Carry on correspondence on a multiplicity of subjects. Prepare commentaries on books of Scripture.

Idelette was constantly amazed at the extraordinary efforts of intellectual toil her husband was capable of putting forth. He humored his weak constitution only to the extent that when he had a free morning he studied reclining in his bed. She would bring him five or six books with which he would occupy himself. He seldom ate any breakfast — in fact indulged in only one meal a day. She would succeed at times in persuading him to have a hot drink. He did permit himself a short break in his studies by walking to and fro in his room for a quarter of an hour a day.

Idelette's first marriage with Jean Stordeur had been quite different. Occasionally when the shop was closed her husband would do some work at home — some carving in wood or ivory; but this home work did not demand such close concentration that they would not be able to share most of their evenings talking together.

Idelette did not complain for she felt that in a quiet way, by her failure to reproach her husband or resent his busy days, she was a part of his great work. Still, it made her very happy one evening when he pushed aside his books and came to seek her.

"Let us walk by the lake this evening, Idelette."

"Is Madame Kuhn worse?"

"I do not know."

"You mean we are not going visiting the sick?"

"This walk shall be taken for pure pleasure." Her husband's voice bristled.

They strolled together by the blue lake, pausing to feed the swans. And Genevan eyebrows lifted and friends smiled to see Jean Calvin pleasure-walking with his wife.

"Are you enjoying yourself?" Idelette asked anxiously.

"Very much. And you?"

"My conscience troubles me," said his wife.

"Why?"

"I am burdened with the feeling I am keeping you from God's work."

"This is God's work." Then seeing the bewilderment on his wife's face he explained, "It is a husband's duty to spend time with his wife and family."

"Beware! I shall hold you to those words."

"You threaten!"

"I do."

He smiled down at her, "So little and so frightening a wife I have chosen." He crumbled a piece of bread for a gull and threw it in the air. The swift bird swooped down and caught the fragment in mid-air. "Do I neglect you, Idelette?"

"Why do you ask?"

"That is no answer."

"If you ever do I know it is for God's work. I would not have it otherwise."

"You are a good wife."

Idelette was pleased with his rare praise. "But why, Jean, why all these questions?"

"I have been very severely scolded today for my neglect of you."

"How dare anyone interfere in what is our private affair?"

"This one has every right."

"Who spoke to you about the matter?"

"God."

"What did He say?"

"He spoke as always through His revealed will. I was reading the first chapter of Corinthians, the seventh chapter, and the third verse, '*Que le mari rende á sa femme la bienveillance.*' Let the man render unto his wife true friendship.'"

"And what did you reply?"

"I said, 'I will.'"

And so it became no longer an uncommon sight to see Monsieur and Madame Calvin strolling together of an evening. For God had spoken.

16

It was early in January that Idelette knew she was with child. It had been more than a year since her marriage, and she was beginning to fear this second marriage was to be barren. For days she went about with an inner radiance. This would be the third child she had carried, and yet in a way this pregnancy was different from both the others.

Idelette had loved Jean Stordeur, but she had never felt any unusual anticipation or expectation from any offspring they would have. Neither of them possessed in any measure a spark of genius. But during the year she had been the wife of the brilliant reformer Idelette had become increasingly aware that Jean Calvin was a man of the ages. This was his child — from it, surely, one could expect greatness.

But in spite of her exaltation Idelette found herself lapsing into moments of deep foreboding. Because of this gloom she was at first reluctant to share her good news with her husband. But as the months passed and all went well, she decided it was foolish to fear any longer that all her hopes would end in disappointment and she shared her anticipations with him.

Her moment of revelation came as quietly as all the great epochs in their lives together. They were discussing a new problem which had arisen in the rules governing the lives of the citizens of Geneva. It was one of the many small annoyances which was plaguing Jean at the time. He hated the way in which the good Protestant families persisted in calling their children by the names of saints. He had that day refused to baptize a child Christophe. And the family had been indignant.

"We must post a list of banned names for children," he had stated finally.

"Then please do not put 'Jacques' on the list."

"Jacques? There is nothing heretical about 'Jacques.' It is a good name."

"I'm glad you think so, Jean," she had replied demurely. "Next September it would make me very happy if you would baptize your son by that name."

Jean Calvin said nothing. She watched the look of wonder creep over his expressive face. He came to her, placed his slender hand on her shoulder, but still he did not speak. He walked quietly to his own private study and closed the door. Idelette sat where she was. She knew she had made him happier than she had ever succeeded in doing before. Yet he had not stayed with her. She understood him so well. She knew that he had obeyed his first impulse — to thank God for this gift alone in the sanctuary of his study. Idelette knew she had no human rival for the affections of her husband. Wistfully she wondered, "Could a woman be jealous of God?"

17

"Mama, why does Monsieur Viret call his wife 'chou-chou'?"

Idelette smiled. "Because he loves her very much. He uses the word as an affectionate nickname."

"I don't think I would like to be called a 'little cabbage' by my husband. Does my father, also, call you such names?"

"No. Your father is not given to nicknames. Men, my child, are different in the way they show their affection. You are not too young to learn that. You must never judge by appearances."

"I have noticed that they are different. Monsieur Bucer would place his arm about the waist of his wife. I have never seen my father do that."

"And I am quite sure you never will." Idelette smiled. "Your father is more sedate and proper in his manners than Monsieur Bucer — I have no complaints!" Idelette picked up a brush from the table and began to unbraid her daughter's thick black hair.

"Is it true, Mama, what they say?"

"Is what true?" Jean Calvin came into the bedroom and sank relaxed in his prized armchair.

"That mama is going to have a baby?"

Jean Calvin raised his eyebrows. Idelette stopped her brushing.

"Madame Frachebourg asked me," Judith added as if she felt some explanation for her question were owing.

Jean Calvin smiled. Madame Frachebourg, the local midwife, was evidently trying to line up some business.

"It is true," said Idelette. "You will soon have a brother or a sister."

"When, tomorrow?"

Idelette suppressed a smile. "Go to your father's study and fetch his calendar."

Judith, the sedate, ran to get it. Her tiny bare feet caught and tripped on her long nightgown. She almost plunged headlong in her eagerness. It was good to see her so interested. Idelette took Judith on her lap and slowly turned the pages of the calendar. When she came to the month of September Idelette placed a finger on the first day of the month and had the child circle it.

"Maybe then."

Judith's face fell. "That is almost as far away as Christmas."

"Almost. But it will give us the necessary time to get ready for the baby."

The brushing continued. Monsieur Calvin rested his head against the back of the chair. It was pleasant to relax in this environment of peaceful domesticity after a hard day.

"Mother!"

"Yes, my child."

"May I have a baby, too?"

Jean Calvin coughed. Idelette kept on brushing. "Someday, no doubt you will."

"I don't mean someday; I mean now."

"You would make a good mother to a baby, little Judith, for you love children. But you see every child must have not only a mother but also a father."

"Oh!" said Judith, and her questions stopped.

Children were so different, Idelette thought. Judith was so easy to satisfy. Now when Charles had first wondered about the origin of life he had pushed her back until he knew the whole truth. Idelette did not believe in giving any more information than was requested. The truth could be unfolded when the child asked for each new step of revelation.

God must have given a special instinct to mothers, thought Jean Calvin. He was glad Judith had not pressed him for any answers. Idelette was not only a remarkable wife, but a good mother. He could not have chosen better for the mother of his child.

18

Because Idelette went her way serenely, most people — even her husband — were unaware of the many rebellious thoughts she harbored which never reached the surface. Seldom did anger break through her rigid self control. But once he was its target.

Perhaps the most constant of the many guests who frequented the Calvin house were the Aumonts. They were distant relatives of Idelette, and presumed because of it on the hospitality of the Calvin home. Their visit in early April threatened to break all previous records. Jean Calvin's patience — never his strong point — was exhausted, for the work in his study was piled high. Idelette's strength, he knew, should not be taxed at this time by any unnecessary demands. Even Judith was growing petulant from so much unsought attention.

One day, while Idelette was out, he decided the time had come for direct action. He pointed out to the Aumonts with clarity that their extended visit was imposing a hardship on Idelette which he was loath to have her shoulder. He had hoped any unpleasantness which might result from his necessary frankness would have dissipated before Idelette returned. But unfortunately Madame Aumont was still fuming at the indignity she had suffered when Idelette entered the living room. Jean took from his wife her basket of groceries and tried to edge her into the kitchen. But he could not escape his indignant guest.

"We are leaving, Idelette."

Idelette, surprised but relieved at the news, said hospitably, "You will surely eat with us before you go."

"We are not invited to sup with you," was the cold reply. Both men looked acutely embarrassed, but said nothing.

Idelette looked from one to the other, "I don't understand."

"I have explained to the Aumonts," said Jean Calvin at least somewhat apologetically, "that their stay here. . . ."

"Your husband has made it clear that our presence here is an imposition."

Monsieur Aumont firmly took his wife's arm and pulled her from the house, but not before the enraged woman was able to throw back one last angry remark over her shoulder, "I am sorry for you, Idelette, married to a —" Her words broke off, as if a hand had been clamped over her mouth.

The Calvins stood in awkward silence until the sound of the footsteps on the cobblestones faded in the distance.

"Madame Aumont," reproached Idelette, "is my childhood friend."

"Does that entitle her to eternal refuge beneath my roof?"

Idelette moved her reproach from the realm of the personal to that of the biblical, "Is it not a divine command to practice hospitality?"

"Are you trying to convince me that we have been 'entertaining angels unawares'?" he said tartly. "You must never take a good verse out of the context of the entire biblical teachings. We have other obligations which take prior consideration: my work, your health. Must all these be sacrificed upon the altar of a childhood friendship which, in my opinion, would have been better if it had not matured?"

"But to show a guest the door!"

"It is done, Idelette. You must trust my judgment in

this. If I did wrongly, the blame is mine alone. Let us speak no more about it. I am hungry."

"Hungry? You think of your stomach at a time like this?"

"Could there be a more appropriate time? It is already five minutes past the dinner hour," he chided her.

His indignant wife left the room. But she did not head for the kitchen. Instead she went into the bedroom, slammed the door, and dropped the latch. Cross and hungry, Jean Calvin called out to her. There was no answer. How could what seemed to him such a trivial matter upset this serene wife of his so disproportionately? Jean Calvin was completely bewildered. Something had had to be done about the Aumonts and he had done it.

Idelette heard the front door close. What was wrong with her? Why was she behaving this way? The Aumonts had become a nuisance. Why should she be so resentful with her husband for dispatching them? And how had she, Idelette Calvin, dared to flaunt her husband? A sermon of his on the place of women in the home came to her mind with its rebuke. His texts had been, "Obey your husband in the Lord," and "And as for the wife, see that she reverence her husband."

"Mother! Mother!" Judith was calling her. Idelette tidied herself and went down to fix the child her supper. Jean did not return. Idelette completed the usual bedtime routine with Judith. Long after the child was asleep Idelette lay awake awaiting her husband's return. Indignation was still uppermost in her feelings. It was after all she who bore the main burden of the constant flow of guests who visited them. How could her husband dismiss one of them without at least consulting her? It was unjust, unkind. Did he have the right? Had she "reverenced her husband" in this action of his? Had she "obeyed him in the Lord"? Jean had explained that he felt his action was the right one. It had been a domestic decision which he, at least, felt was "in the

Lord." Did she have the right of Queen Vashti then to dis-
regard her husband?

Her thoughts troubled her. She still had reached no
decision in her own mind as to her future attitude when she
heard her husband's firm step on the stairs. She feigned sleep
and hoped it would suffice to postpone any immediate reopening of the quarrel.

Jean Calvin gingerly tried the door and was somewhat
surprised and relieved when it yielded to his pressure. As
his eyes became accustomed to the darkness he could see
his wife. Her eyes were firmly closed — too firmly for
natural sleep. For a moment he was tempted to yield and let
the matter rest until morning. Instead he decided to fight
any cowardice on his part and walked with deliberateness
to her side of the bed and sat down.

"I know you are not sleeping, Idelette."

She opened her big eyes and looked at him but said
nothing.

"Your behavior tonight was most unseemly."

His understatement of the fact took her aback. He
continued slowly choosing his words with care. "I, more than
anyone else, am fully aware that I am often hasty in my
actions and in my speech. Perhaps I am not without guilt in
this matter. I can only repeat I am responsible to God for
my behavior — not to you. He is my Judge — He will punish.
But in the divine plan you are responsible to God and also
to me because of the authority He has delegated to me over
you as your husband. I am the head of this home, and I
expect and demand obedience and reverence of all its members 'in the Lord.'"

His words were, Idelette realized, almost completely
lifted from his sermon on the place of women in the home.
It was the same sermon that she had been meditating about.
Her husband calmly, deliberately, went on to outline its
contents for her private edification. He left little doubt
about her wifely duties.

When he finished, Idelette remained silent. Seeing he

had failed to arouse any response from her, he did not press the matter further but left the room for his study. Idelette could hear him crumpling papers and knew that his work was not going well. She hated herself for causing him this unnecessary disturbance. Her husband hewed the line so straight — no deviations were possible for Jean Calvin even for reasons of the heart. God's Word was followed wherever it was explicit in every detail of life — even in matters domestic.

At last she could remain silent no longer. She placed a wool shawl over her shoulders — for the night air was chilly — and went into the study. A small fire burned on the grate. Her husband lay with his head on the desk and did not notice her enter. Idelette went out again quietly and going to the kitchen warmed a bowl of cauliflower soup.

"You haven't eaten tonight, Jean." She offered him the steaming soup she had brought with her. He lifted his head. "Please eat." She set the bowl timidly before him.

"Are you sure this is the time to eat?" He had not forgotten her insubordination.

Idelette flushed. "Please forgive my rudeness. I am still not convinced that your action was right. But you have made me realize that any rebuke should not come from me."

"That is all that is required of you. I want no slavish obedience. Would it make you happy if I told you that I am not sure I did right? And that since there is doubt in my mind, and I know my own disposition to easy irritability, I shall write the Aumonts an apology and invite them to visit us again soon."

Idelette looked at the unhappy face of her husband and broke into laughter. "Let us not carry repentance too far!"

19

The six months which Pierre Viret had promised to serve with Jean Calvin in Geneva went all too swiftly. Idelette hated to see her friend leave. Madame Viret wept when the moment of parting came. "I feel as if I should stay and see you through the birth of the baby, Idelette."

"And what would Pierre do without you?"

Elizabeth Viret blushed. "We have never been apart since our marriage. Pierre would perhaps survive, but I do not know how I could ever live without him. But if you need me. . . ."

Idelette laughed. "I should ask you and have your death on my conscience!"

"I have bungled in my offer. . . ."

"There is not the slightest need to make it, dear friend. I would be as unhappy as you if you did not accompany Pierre. Besides Martin and Elizabeth Bucer are planning to visit Geneva about the time of the baby's arrival. I shall have her with me. And they are going to bring Charles with them."

"What wonderful news!"

"The very best."

"You have missed him so, haven't you, Idelette?"

"I have never stopped longing for him."

"What a happy time that will be for you all. And how does Charles feel about the expected baby?"

"My sister-in-law writes that he is delighted with the news. It may well be the wedge that will cement our family together again. Charles is very like his own father. He has a way with creatures and small children, and they reciprocate his open adoration."

"May I come in?" Pierre called through the open doorway. "I am bringing a small parting present for you — that is for the expected infant."

Idelette was delighted when she saw what Pierre was carrying. It was a tiny carved walnut cradle. "I slept in it as a baby," said Pierre.

Idelette demurred. "Then you must not give such an heirloom to us. Please, Pierre, keep it for your own children."

A shadow fell across Madame Viret's face. "No, no, it is yours. I cannot give birth to a living child." She rushed on, "We could think of no one we would rather give it to."

Idelette placed an arm about her friend's waist, "Thank you with all my heart. I shall borrow it. But someday, I shall bring the cradle to you in Lausanne. Wait and see!"

Elizabeth Viret delayed her friend as they reached the stairs and Pierre went down ahead of them to rejoin Jean in the living room. "Idelette," Madame Viret was tearful again. "You will come and visit me soon and bring the baby. How I long to hold your child in my arms. I feel I have failed Pierre so utterly not to be able to bear his child — this will be a comfort to me to enjoy yours."

Idelette embraced her friend. "Lausanne will be our very first outing. I promise you. But you must not feel you have failed Pierre. You must never feel that way. When we waited, it seemed to me, so long for our child, Jean said to me, 'God makes the grass to grow. Fertility is the gift of God. Offspring are in God's hand.'"

Madame Viret wiped her eyes. "Idelette, you are so good for me. Promise me, will you please, if anything happens to me to care for Pierre. We are so dependent upon each other — more so because there are no children to divert our affection."

"Of course, I will. But you are so full of forebodings. Cheer up, my friend. Do not worry needlessly. Do not permit your devotion to your husband to make you seek shadows that do not exist. I have never known you to be so full of sorrow. Be happy again in your love for God and your love for Pierre."

Madame Viret kissed her friend on the cheek. "I shall. I shall, dearest Idelette. Only remember your promise." Idelette helped her tie her bonnet around her tear-stained face, for her friend was made clumsy by her mood. Then placing her cape about her shoulders the two women went down the stairs together.

But Elizabeth Viret's anxiety was contagious. As the carriage disappeared down the street Idelette found herself saying to Jean, "Shall I ever see her again?"

Jean Calvin laughed. "You women make too much of parting. Lausanne is only a good horseback ride from Geneva. I shall teach you to ride after the child is born, and you may gallop over at will."

"I shall like that," said Idelette. "I shall like that very much."

20

Ami Porral, burgomaster of Geneva, and a staunch friend of the Reformation, was dying. His pastors and Jean Calvin had visited him several times during the morning, expecting any moment to be his last. But still he lingered, and finally they relaxed their constant vigil.

Idelette, who always made it a point to visit the aged and sick, came that afternoon to find the man without any pastoral visitors. One look at the color of his face and Idelette — to whom death was no stranger — recognized its nearness. No one, thought Idelette, should have to face death, that last enemy, alone. She put down the broth she had brought him, and leaning over the dying man she assured him she would stay with him to the end. "Not chance, but the admirable counsel of God has sent me to aid you."

The old intrepid champion of Genevan liberty blessed her for her kindness and found courage in her strength and nearness. Idelette opened the French Bible which lay on the bedstand and read in her clear voice from the fourteenth chapter of John, "*Que votre coeur ne se trouble point. Croyez en Dieu, et croyez en moi. Il y a plusieurs demeures dans la maison de mon Père. . . .*" She stopped reading only when she noticed that his eyes had closed, his jaws had relaxed. Ami Porral was dead. When the pastors and Jean Calvin returned to give the burgomaster further consolation they found it was no longer needed.

Jean walked home with his wife. "It was very good of you to stay, Idelette. Was it difficult?"

Idelette walked slowly by his side. Her breathing was labored. Her baby expected in a few months now made the hill walk to Canon St. a difficult one. She stopped to answer, "Yes. But I felt I could not leave him, Jean. His death was easy. He died while I was reading the Word of God to him."

"It was a fitting close to a great man's life," said her husband.

He put an arm under hers to help her up the steep hill. His wife never ceased to stir his admiration. Idelette, the unexpected! She was a good wife, a good mother, and now she had shone in another role. She was an angel of mercy. It was one of the few times in his life that he recorded a work of Idelette in a letter to a friend. She had performed a gracious act for Ami Porral, and in doing so had bound her husband closer to her.

21

The Calvin baby was due in September. In June of that year the dark shadow of plague fell over the city of Geneva. Panic broke out; for it was alleged that the disease was being spread by witches. How else could one account for the plague's epidemic proportions? Scarcely a home was spared. The Council of Geneva acted with firmness, and in all thirty-four witches were executed.

One of the women suspected of the diabolical spreading of the plague was Mother Frachebourg. She had been seen, reported an informer, spitting on the door of the L'Oiseaux family, and all its members had subsequently perished in agony.

Idelette, who seldom intervened in the political affairs of Geneva, begged her husband for the life of the old woman, "Jean, you must save her."

"Even if she is guilty?"

"She couldn't be guilty. Madame Frachebourg is a foolish garrulous old woman. But she is not devil-possessed."

"Then do not fear for her. She will have a fair trial, and the Council will find her innocent."

"Is the Council always infallible in its judgments?"

"No human agency is infallible; but the Council is fair and just. Are you yourself, Idelette, approaching this trial devoid of prejudice?"

"Call it prejudice if you will. But I feel as I do because

I know the character of Madame Frachebourg. I have seen her too often helping at the time of childbirth and seen her tender care of a newborn infant. I know she would not wilfully harm a living soul. And to stoop to such vileness as to deliberately spread this horrible disease! I shall go and testify myself in her behalf." Idelette spoke with spirit.

"If you feel your own plea would be more effective than my own, I shall yield my place to you."

"Oh, Jean! I did not know you were planning to speak for her. I thought — "

"Tell me, what did you think?"

"You are always so just, so rational. You never let your heart influence any of your decisions."

"Justice is justice only when it is dispassionate."

"But death is so final."

"Yes. And they who kill must be taught that lesson."

"That sounds so harsh."

Jean Calvin flinched. "Idelette, no one welcomes these executions. But the spread of the 'Black Death' must be stopped, and these evil-doers — tools of Satan — must pay for their dastardly acts with their lives. These wicked people are going to plague victims and dipping their hands into the open sores in order to smear this infected pus on the doors of the innocent. And you think death is too severe a penalty for such carrion! What of the innocent who writhe in agony because of them and die in torment? Is burning the evil ones not justice? What punishment would you suggest?"

Idelette hesitated. "Banishment?"

"Banishment! Idelette! How evil that would be. It would only turn loose on other innocent neighborhoods those who had filled their cup full of iniquity in Geneva. No, the penalty for witchcraft must be death."

Although Monsieur and Madame Calvin disagreed on a suitable punishment for the crime neither of them questioned the fact that the women were witches. In Geneva of that day one assumed the existence of witches.

To Idelette's joy, however, Monsieur Calvin as a character witness for the defense saved Madame Frachebourg from being branded a witch; and it was to his intervention that she owed her life. In time, away from the shadow of the faggots, Madame Frachebourg even grew to jest about her trial. It was, she liked to relate with her grim humor, a very efficient cure for spitting.

22

By July the plague had devastated Europe. It was especially severe in Strasbourg. Idelette worried endlessly about her boy Charles. Elizabeth Bucer had promised to come to be with Idelette to help her with the arrival of the expected child in September, and the plan had been for young Charles to accompany the Bucers to rejoin the Calvin family at that time. Idelette regretted allowing the boy to remain in Strasbourg so long. If only she had insisted that Charles accompany her and Judith to Geneva.

Ann Calvin, Antoine's wife, came bursting into the home on Canon St. with the bad news. Elizabeth Bucer and four of her children had died of the plague.

"And Charles? What of Charles? Have you any news of him?" asked the frantic mother.

"None. But they say half the city is dead."

Jean Calvin joined the women in the living room in time to hear Ann's rash statement. "Ann, you must not repeat stories unless you are sure of their accuracy." He was unusually harsh in his rebuke of his sister-in-law. His wife's pallor alarmed him. He had been trying to keep the sad news of the Bucer deaths from her; he had not thought to muzzle his attractive sister-in-law.

"Is it not true then, Jean? Is Elizabeth not dead?" Idelette's voice was hopeful.

"I am very sorry, Idelette, but that part of Ann's news

is true. As to half the city perishing I doubt if the plague is that severe. And as for Charles, so far as we know, he is well. Your brother and Antoinette have taken a small house in a neighboring village. You know they will run no risks with the boy."

"Poor, poor Martin." Idelette wept for her bereaved friend and for her own loss.

"Save your tears for yourself," Ann continued refusing to be daunted by Jean Calvin's scowls. "Did you know that your own husband has offered to serve as chaplain at the Plague Lazar outside our city gates?"

Idelette shivered. All of the plague victims in Geneva were accommodated as far as possible in this hospital isolated from the others. Idelette knew that among the staff who served these poor souls was a chaplain. This chaplain was selected by the ministers of Geneva and appointed by the Council. Some ministers refused the appointment. All dreaded it. "Must you, Jean?" Idelette pleaded.

"One can never refuse an appointment of danger with honor merely because it is hazardous. Surely you would not want to deprive those poor souls of every earthly comfort?"

"You see!" interjected Ann. "I told you so. He is quite mad."

Idelette turned with alarm. "Jean, surely if the Council appointed you, you would refuse."

"You would have me betray my calling?"

"I do not urge you to this action for purely personal reasons — not for myself alone or even for the sake of the unborn child. But your work — who could take your place?"

"No human is indispensable in God's program. And I must run the risk when my turn comes. I could not fail those who need my ministry. But do not be needlessly upset, Idelette. No decisions have been made. It is in the hands of God. Come, you must rest."

Jean Calvin urged his wife to lie down. With firmness he maneuvered Ann Calvin out of the house. But when he himself left to return to the Council chambers Idelette, left alone, became more worried and depressed. She found it impossible to lie quietly in her own room. Feeling that some manual work would serve as an antidote she decided to fetch the day's supply of water from the spring. As she set the bucket down upon the kitchen table a sharp pain caused her to clutch her side. She dragged herself up the flight of stairs to her bedroom and fell across the bed.

Idelette had not dreaded the hour of the baby's birth. Both of her earlier children had arrived safely without undue pain. But this time something was wrong. The baby should not be born yet for several months, and these pains she was feeling were not the mild pre-birth pangs she knew so well. They were coming sharp and fast. She pressed her fingers into her sides, hoping she was mistaken, and that the contractions would stop. But when the pains fell into the regularity of pattern she knew so well and scarcely any time elapsed between them, she clutched frantically to the walnut headboard of the bed and dragged herself upright to go for help. It was then she saw Judith. The child was standing wide-eyed in the doorway. "Go, fetch Madame Frachebourg, quick!"

The child disappeared immediately. Relieved that help was on its way Idelette lay alone now with the pain. Things were not going well — this she knew. She touched the small wooden cradle by her bed as if to give her confidence. Would help never come? She lost consciousness before the mid-wife arrived and was delirious for days after the birth. She kept calling Madame Frachebourg, Elizabeth, and did not recognize her own husband. But on the fifth day the clouds lifted and she saw her own room, the walnut bed and the cradle that Pierre Viret had given her. Was it empty? She called out in fear, and someone placed the baby in her arms. The child was alive. God be praised! She pressed her lips gently over the dark fuzzy hair. The skin on the little forehead was wrinkled, and she smoothed it gently with her long fingers. God was great and God was good. There was no death here. She and the child had both passed through the valley of the shadow. She was alive and she had her baby.

Jean was beside her smiling. She had not noticed him before. He cupped her face in his long slender fingers. His eyes were tired and sleepless. "We have our son, Idelette, our baby Jacques."

Mother Frachebourg came to take the child from her, but Idelette clung to the boy. "Let her keep the child," Jean said curtly.

Idelette cradled the tiny one closer, still haunted by the shadows through which they had so recently passed. And then she slept again.

On Tuesday, the child was baptized. Idelette was still weak, but well enough to walk the few steps to the church. On Wednesday, the child died. It was during the night Idelette heard a tiny whimper. She bent over the cradle. There was no sound — not even the soft whisper of breath. The little one had simply ceased to breathe.

All that night Idelette kept her lonely vigil, the dead child held in her arms. It was dawn when Jean awakened and seeing what had happened gently pried her fingers apart and took the tiny body from her. Jean wrote his dear friend, Pierre Viret, "The Lord has certainly inflicted a severe and bitter wound in the death of our infant son. But He is Himself a father, and knows what is good for His children." It was God's hand that had taken Jacques. The Lord had given, the Lord had taken.

Idelette made no murmur. But she could not eat nor sleep. Weakened by the birth she failed to gain back any strength.

"You must make more effort to get well, Idelette. Your lack of will is holding you back," her grieving husband urged her.

"Your child! I cannot understand." Idelette wept. "How could God take your child? Mine, yes. I am not worthy. But you, you who have always served Him so selflessly. I cannot understand."

Jean placed a firm hand over his wife's mouth. "We deserve nothing good from God, Idelette. We are all sinners. Every gift is of grace. I would much rather, my dearest wife, have my child in the bosom of God than here in our home — if that be His will. You must not grieve so deeply. There will be, if God is gracious, another child."

"I fear there will be no other . . ."

"That too, is in God's hands. If I shall never know the joy of a son of my flesh, I shall be content. God has blessed me richly with thousands of sons of the spirit. I would not have it otherwise."

Idelette found comfort in his words. But when they laid the tiny body to rest in the cemetery of Plain Palais it was as if they were burying a part of her. She was never completely healthy again and seldom without pain. And Jean watched over her with a new tenderness. It was as if he, too, sensed the fact that the angel of death had not completely departed from this house.

23

Pierre Dagnet was now a member of the household of Jean Calvin. He served as Monsieur Calvin's secretary and was able to relieve him of countless time-consuming chores which, before his arrival, had dissipated much of the Reformer's strength. Appreciating all that this new secretary meant to him Jean burst forth enthusiastically to his wife, "I don't know how I ever managed without him."

"Without whom?" asked Idelette, searching for the context of her husband's remark.

"Monsieur Dagnet, who else?" Jean Calvin was always impatient when he had to make what he considered an unnecessary explanation.

"Who else, of course?" said Idelette.

Jean Calvin overlooked the irony in his wife's voice. He was warming to his subject, "He is a prince among men."

His wife agreed with him, "He is also without exception the most lovable man I have known."

"Without exception?" demurred her husband.

"Pierre Viret could challenge that title perhaps," conceded his wife.

"Viret? And what of Calvin?" Jean countered.

Idelette laughed. It pleased her when her husband indulged his wry sense of humor. She fully enjoyed playing the game. "Calvin? I love him. But with all due charity, could I call him lovable?"

"Humpf! I prayed for humility and God sent me an honest wife!" They exchanged a marital glance full of amusement and affection.

"Will he bring us bad luck?" asked Judith.

"Judith!" reprimanded her father. "You know there is no such thing as bad luck."

"Wherever did you hear such a statement?" Her mother wisely pried, knowing her daughter well enough to know the sentiment must have been planted by an adult hand.

"Madame Frachebourg said hunchbacks always bring bad luck, and that Monsieur, my father, was very unwise to choose one for his secretary."

"Madame Frachebourg's brush with death has not chastened her tongue sufficiently." Jean Calvin was angry. Idelette hated to see his joyous mood dissolved and have him, irritated, leave the room. The child, innocent of being the cause of her father's withdrawal, pursued the subject with her mother.

"Why is Monsieur Dagnet hunchbacked, mama?"

"I do not know what caused his deformity," answered her mother.

"I shall ask him," said the child.

"No, Judith. That would be unkind. Never permit yourself to notice anyone who is crippled or in any way different from you. Never even think of it. When you see Monsieur Dagnet, do not look at his hump, but remind yourself that he is a fine man — kinder and more loving than most."

The docile child did as she was directed. And Monsieur Calvin's secretary, who had become accustomed to the stares and jibes of the cruel young, was surprised at the lack of interest Judith showed in his deformity and was grateful. It was as if when he entered the Calvin house on Canon St. he left his crippled back outside the door.

24

The long journey by carriage to Strasbourg was almost ended. Idelette was very tired. She rested her head back against the plush cushion and shut her eyes trying to shut out the jolting scenery. The wheels rumbled along the rough road. There was a sudden lurch and she was flung forward.

"Are you hurt, Madame?"

"No. I'm quite all right. What happened?"

"I am afraid we have a broken spoke in our right wheel. It will cause us several hours' delay. We are not within walking distance of any inn."

"Do not fret for me, Monsieur Dagnet." Idelette reassured her husband's secretary. Since her husband's duties would not permit his absence from Geneva at this time she had been grateful when it had been arranged that Pierre Dagnet make the long journey with her.

But Monsieur Dagnet could not help fretting. He had a sensitivity which his own handicap had inbred into him. He did not like the idea of the fragile Idelette exposed for hours to the chilly Alpine air. It would blow colder now that the sun was almost gone. It was with great relief that he saw a carriage coming down the road. It stopped behind them and a courteous, well-dressed man stepped down and offered his help. When the newcomer learned that the stranded travelers were headed for Strasbourg he insisted on helping Madame Calvin into his own carriage to continue the journey with him. Gratefully Pierre Dagnet watched them leave before he turned to fix the broken wheel.

"You are very kind to trouble yourself in my behalf, Monsieur."

"I am at your service, Madame," the stranger replied courteously. "My driver will be happy to drive you directly to your destination."

"I am planning to visit my brother, Charles de Bure, of Strasbourg. His home is not far from the Petite Eglise of St. Nicolas."

"When we enter the city if you give me directions . . ." The stranger looked directly at Idelette. "You are not well, Madame. Pardon my interference, but should you be traveling in your condition? You see I am a physician, and it entitles me to a certain impertinence in others' affairs."

Idelette smiled at him. "I should not be traveling; but the urgency is so great. You see, Monsieur, my son lives with my brother and I have not seen him for two years. Another year, my health would perhaps be worse rather than better. I dared not take the risk and postpone the trip."

"How old is your son, Madame?"

"He is not yet thirteen."

"He does not live with you, Madame?"

Idelette flushed. "I am hoping he will return with me. He has been visiting with my brother. I did not know that the visit would last so long. But illness and death have kept us apart. Two years, Monsieur, and he was so small when I left Strasbourg. Will he know me, do you think?"

"A heart, even a young heart, Madame, does not forget."

"You are very comforting, Monsieur. You have a family of your own?"

"Yes. But I seldom see them."

She looked her query. "I am a doomed man, Madame. I am an exile, with no home. I am always in flight. I have been condemned to the flames by the Church of Rome. I am dead to my homeland. I may never return."

"I am sorry for you."

"You give pity to a heretic?"

"My husband, too, is an exile from home. A dear friend of ours bears on his back the lance scar inflicted by a priest. Many are in your company — heretics from Rome."

The rough road caused the carriage to lurch. To steady herself Idelette rested her hand on the seat between them. It fell on a manuscript lying there. "You have been writing, Monsieur. Your chivalry to me is interfering with your work."

"It is perhaps as well. What I write will be no great gift to the world."

"Is the article for some medical publication?"

The stranger leafed through the pages. "It is a theological treatise, Madame."

"Theological?"

"You are interested?"

"Who is not in the things pertaining to God?"

"Who is?"

"You are bitter, Monsieur le docteur."

"Should I not be? For my medical views I have been disbarred. Now I turn to thoughts of God, and here too the boundaries are fixed. Any new thought is *ipso facto* heretical."

"Is it branded false because it is new, Monsieur, or because it is false?"

"Does it matter? Who is concerned to search out truth? How many are there who open their eyes to a fair examination of their beliefs in God. They shudder at even the possibility of a hell and make a crutch of God and hobble away from the flames."

"And you would snatch this crutch from them?"

"Men should walk upright unaided by vain delusions."

"We are of one mind, Monsieur — if these hopes be vain."

"Do you mean, Madame, that you would not cling to a lie if it gave you comfort?"

"No, Monsieur, I would not. If the crutch be false, I would have none of it."

"You have an independent mind, Madame. I believe you. I shall send you a copy of my work when it is finished." He meticulously wrote down her name and address. The usually observant Idelette failed to notice the start the physician gave when he heard her name.

"And you, Monsieur. May I, too, have your name and address. I should like to send you a work on apologetics by my husband. If you, too, have an independent mind, will you read it?"

"That will not be necessary, Madame. I already have many of the works of your illustrious husband."

The carriage rumbled down the streets of Strasbourg. It was not until her courteous host had helped her into the home of her brother and driven away that Idelette, in consternation, realized that she had failed to register his name. It had been a deliberate oversight on the part of her host, Michel de Villeneuve, alias Michael Servetus.

25

There was no doubt about the fact that Charles was very happy living with his uncle and aunt. Idelette could not help feeling depressed. She had never realized how much she had counted on finding a lonesome Charles, one who would be wanting to return to Geneva with her. When she saw him cheerful in his Strasbourg surroundings, so like the Charles who used to fill the Stordeur home with laughter, her hopes vanished. It was the lot of women to bear and lose their sons. But he was still so young to be torn from her.

In all fairness, however, she could not help but feel grateful to the brother who had so successfully weaned her son away from her. He was a better boy and an obedient one. His sullenness had vanished. He inquired politely about his step-father. She knew that he would obey her. If she insisted he would return to Geneva with her. But when she saw the intimate bond of affection between her brother and her son she feared she would not have the heart to break it. She postponed momentarily any final decision and abandoned herself to the pleasure of being reunited with her loved ones.

Idelette's son did all he could to make her visit to Strasbourg a memorable one. He exerted all that charm which he had possessed in abundance from the cradle. Mother and son walked arm in arm down the city streets.

They took their favorite walk across the wooden bridge over the Ill river and traced its course back to the two arms which cut the city into an island. They fed their favorite swans. They wandered by the familiar landmarks, the old Stordeur home, the Petite Eglise. Charles — little man that he now was — even inquired seriously about her marriage, "You are happy, mama?" he asked.

Idelette looked at her tall son, at the broad shoulders which had lost their boyish slope, and smiled at his concern, "Yes, my son."

"We hear often that Monsieur Calvin is disliked in Geneva."

"You hear it from discontents who are banished from our city."

"You are loyal."

"My son, try to understand this great man who is your father. He is trying to do a unique thing in Geneva. He is attempting to apply the laws of God to a commonwealth on earth. That task could not make any man beloved by all."

As she spoke of her husband her heart was filled with tenderness and longing. She knew that her visit could not be prolonged much longer. She wanted to hurry back to Geneva and Jean.

"Your father is always concerned for your welfare. Remember, if you ever need a friend, you can find none truer. I shall not insist on your return, Charles. You are doing a good work here in Strasbourg, and you are growing into a man of whom I am proud."

Even as she spoke, Idelette started to weep. Her son took her into his arms. As she felt the strength of his young arms she yearned again so much that the pious wish, which had helped her decide to marry Jean Calvin, could yet be fulfilled. She could not bear the thought that her son who could have all the advantages of living day by day with the most brilliant mind of his day preferred to stay with her brother — a good man but one of moderate ability.

Hopefully she asked, "Do you desire to return with me?"

Her son did not want to hurt her. She sensed that by his delayed answer. "If you wish, I shall return with you."

"You do not wish it?"

Forced to answer Charles said quietly, "No, mama."

An unwilling Charles in Geneva? thought Idelette. No, far better that he serve God in this place. How sad to realize that her son, Charles Stordeur, would never fill the ranks when her husband died. Other young men — those others of whom her husband had spoken — those eager, earnest disciples, sons of the spirit, would carry the torch. While her son plodded through life, they would seize the opportunity he spurned and reach the stars.

Resignedly she gave him away, "You may stay, my darling." His arms tightened about her. *This is a memory I must not lose, this moment with my only son,* thought Idelette. *He will never be a great man. But, with God's help, he can be a good one.*

26

The day that Idelette returned to Geneva was sunny and invigorating as only a Swiss morning can be. The mountain air was bracing. Monsieur Calvin breathed in deeply and exhaled deliberately as he paced back and forth past the stable door where the carriage from Strasbourg would come to its final stop. Idelette saw him from the carriage window. How good it was to be home.

Jean Calvin helped her down the steep carriage step and took her small bag from the driver.

"Did you have a good trip?" he asked politely.

"Yes, thank you," she replied demurely. "Is Judith not with you?"

"Only doting husbands get up at five in the morning to meet the carriage of Monsieur Gautier — which always arrives at least three hours late," Jean Calvin glared at the driver who shrugged his shoulders philosophically and went into the tavern.

"Have you been waiting long?"

"Three hours."

"But Jean, why? When you know the carriage is always late, why did you arrive so early?"

"I did not come early. I arrived on time."

Idelette smiled, "I beg your pardon. Why did you arrive on time? Did you think your confidence in schedules would alter Monsieur Gautier's habits?"

There was no reply. Monsieur Calvin merely looked unhappy. "You have had a bad month," his wife said sympathetically.

"No. It has been exceptionally successful."

"Oh!"

"Your visit was pleasant?"

"Yes."

They started to walk slowly up the steep steps, a short cut to the home on Canon St. It was not until they reached their garden that Idelette spoke again. "How I have missed this view! My memory did not do it justice. And the roses are so beautiful. Jean, you did not forget to water them after all."

"You thought I would?"

"I hoped you would," said Idelette.

"You hoped I would. I do not understand. After all your explicit directions."

"I come home to find you have gotten along entirely too well without me. My daughter sleeps tranquilly in bed. My husband is concerned only in the moral laxness of a lazy driver who never keeps his schedule. And the roses still bloom."

"Although Monsieur Gautier did contribute to my peevishness, I was not upset merely by the moral laxness to which he is prone."

"No?" she queried.

They were entering their front door now. With one hand he closed it firmly behind him, and with the other he drew her into his arms. "I was upset," he said emphatically, "first: because the lateness of the carriage delayed this moment which I have so much anticipated; second: because the very first words my wife, after a month's absence, says to me are, 'Where is Judith?'; third: my wife exclaims she has missed the view from the garden; fourth: shall I go on?"

Idelette laughed. "No, please."

"Mama, oh mama! You are home at last!" Jean Calvin

hastily dropped his arm from about his wife's waist. His daughter with an unusual show of affection threw her arms about her mother. "We have missed you so."

"That is good to hear." Idelette threw a chiding glance at her husband. "Have you been a good girl?"

"Oh, yes, mama, very good. And I did not forget to water the roses every day."

It did not seem to Judith that she had said anything particularly humorous, but she joined in, anyway, with the laughter of her parents.

27

Idelette peeled some extra potatoes, put them into the iron pot, covered them with water, and hung the kettle to boil in the fireplace. It was a beautiful Sunday morning. Undoubtedly there would be visitors in the congregation of St. Pierre that morning, and the Calvin table would stretch at the midday meal, as always, to include them — so it was as well to be prepared. Monsieur Calvin never questioned his wife's ability to provide for unexpected guests. It was a compliment to her housewifely ability — one compliment that at times Idelette would have forfeited gladly. This multiplication of the loaves and the fishes without miraculous aid taxed her ingenuity.

Idelette washed her hands and dried them carefully. As she adjusted the coif over her head Judith came in. Idelette's watchful eyes were aware of how very quickly her little girl was growing to young ladyhood. As she helped Judith fix her hair in the simple style worn by the young girls of Geneva she studied her daughter's features. Judith really did not resemble her except in her olive coloring and in her walk. But her quiet manner was so like Idelette's own that strangers often made the mistake of thinking they looked alike.

The women always left the house with plenty of time to spare. Monsieur Calvin went even an hour earlier than they. The walk to the Cathedral of St. Pierre could be done in two minutes and usually was accomplished in this minimum time by the methodical Jean Calvin. The women preferred to stroll. After they closed their garden gate mother and daughter walked down the cobblestone street on the left side, for thus they were afforded a rewarding view of Lake Leman and the Alps which its still waters reflected. At the old spring they jogged right for a few paces, then turned left on the Rue de St. Pierre. Here it was that they usually met Madame Frachebourg panting and out of breath from having reached the street's left intersection with the Rue de Perron. Madame Frachebourg, who lived on the Rue de Perron, tarried at the intersection to catch her breath long enough to intercept the Calvin family every Sunday. Then she would walk with her short jerky steps beside the graceful mother and daughter. It gave the mid-wife of Geneva a feeling of reflected holiness to walk into the church with the family of the much esteemed minister of St. Pierre; and although her pew was not near theirs she was always with them when the narrow street widened into the square which the church dominated.

The Church of St. Pierre was an impressive structure. Unlike the modest Petite Eglise of Strasbourg its edifice towered over the city. It was built on top of the city of Geneva. All other streets rambled around and down from it below to the lake. Shaped like a cross it had two heavy Romanesque towers and one slender Gothic one. It always looked to Idelette to be as solid as the mountains which rose behind it, a church built on a rock, designed to point one upward to the cross.

Idelette and her daughter walked down under the high Gothic arches to sit on the left side of the church four rows from the front. When Monsieur Calvin walked into the side pulpit to speak he towered over his family. Judith would tilt her lovely chin and look at her father as he spoke. She liked to watch him floating as it were above her in his black robe with the flowing sleeves. His capped face was etched against the massive pillar upon which the new carved wooden pulpit was attached. Judith was always fascinated by the emblem over her father's head. It was Jean Calvin's own, a heart held forth in the flame of sacrifice.

Her mother did not look up. Instead she would drop her eyes, or when she lifted them she would look straight ahead at the lovely stained glass window. The shield, the coat of arms of Geneva which was depicted in glass, was an inspiring sight to her. The left yellow half of the shield pictured a black half-eagle with a red crown. This represented the rule of the Duke in the olden days. On the right red half was a yellow key with a red cross on its latch. This reminded the citizens of the rule of the Bishop. Her husband had designated that the three golden letters be placed over the shield: J.H.S. — Jesus Hominum Salvator. Now the coat of arms proclaimed to all Christ was the head of the new theocratic state of Geneva. Under the shield was Jean Calvin's famous three word sermon, "Post tenebras lux!" "After darkness light!"

As Idelette heard the messages of her husband Sunday after Sunday each to her was summarized by this motto. Blessed light illumined her. She preferred to focus on this window or shut her eyes when Jean Calvin preached, and let his voice alone convey the message to her. It disturbed her to look up into the flashing sunken eyes.

But of these private habits of his family Monsieur Calvin was not aware; for when he spoke he directed his look usually to the last row of pews in his sanctuary as if to capture the attention of every last one of his sheep, even those on the fringes. And only an untoward noise on the part of his closer audience would bring his penetrating glance to rest upon them. On rare occasions a crying infant would cause him to pause to rebuke the mother who permitted any prolonged interruption of God's message. Madame Calvin and her daughter were happy to be lost in the anonymity of the crowd.

After the morning service had ended Idelette told her daughter she would have to hurry home to cook dinner, for she had noticed the Fontaine family from Bale had been in the morning congregation. Since her mother's eyes had remained downcast through the whole morning worship, Judith marveled again at how her mother without looking saw everything. She was happy to tarry at the church and be the one to escort the guests to the home on Canon St. Judith loved company.

But this morning Idelette had been wrong. When she heard footsteps coming up the walk and looked out, hidden behind the green shutter, to see how many guests were hers for the day, to her surprise she saw only her husband and daughter walking up the garden path. They made a pretty picture, Judith in a long daffodil yellow frock clinging to Jean's arm. He still wore the black clerical gown with its stiff white collar; and from a distance the pretty child looked almost like a gay boutonniere against his blackness.

How strange to be having Sunday dinner alone. There were very few such meals for the Calvins. In Strasbourg there had always been the pensioners. In Geneva there were always the transients. The necessity for leading a conversation had seldom fallen on Idelette. So many others eagerly had provided the talk about the dinner table. Feeling constrained today to say something — for Jean was silent — she ventured a compliment on the sermon of the morning. Jean's eyebrows raised. "I felt dismally dissatisfied with it myself. There seemed to be much restlessness in the right section of the audience. It disturbed me, and I overlooked two very important points I had intended to make."

Jean Calvin always spoke from memory and never took a note into the pulpit — not even an outline. He did not feel comforted today at his wife's praise. "Were you listening carefully, Idelette?"

Idelette flushed. In all honesty she confessed that she had allowed her thoughts to waver when she had seen the Fontaines from Bale.

"And you proceeded to think of Sunday dinner and the pot boiling on the hearth. Because you did not listen well I was able to satisfy the half hearted attention you gave to me."

"You always look so majestic in your pulpit, father." Judith rashly contributed her sentence to the conversation.

Jean Calvin's eyebrows drew together in displeasure. "I am glad you saw me, my daughter. Now tell me, did you also hear me?"

"Oh yes, father," Judith replied hastily when she saw his face. "It was a lovely sermon." Idelette winced. To-day, even Judith who always sought to please was blundering badly.

"I wasn't aware," said her father sternly, "that the subject of the damnation of the wicked could be considered a 'lovely sermon.' While I, a messenger of God, thunder out denunciations my own daughter thinks of my appearance, and my wife," he spluttered, "envisions potatoes!"

Idelette vainly tried to change the subject, "Why did not the Fontaines return with you?"

"Unfortunately they had other plans and your morning meditations have been wasted," he said sarcastically.

They ate in silence. Then before the thanks for the food was repeated at the end of the meal Monsieur Calvin picked up the subject as if it had never been dropped.

"How many of the people of St. Pierre came to church this morning with disciplined minds to give their full attention to the adoration of their Creator?" Idelette and Judith both hung their heads. "How can I feed sheep who are not hungry, silly inattentive sheep who cannot think on heavenly things with no distractions for one brief hour?"

It was one of the few occasions that Idelette remembered that the family of Jean Calvin had had directed at them a sermon by the greatest preacher of his day. The sermon was not unduly short. When it had finished it was over the heads of a chastened wife and daughter that the benediction for the food was pronounced.

"Dear God," prayed Jean Calvin, "as we thank Thee for this sustenance for our bodies provided by Thy gracious hands, make us truly grateful for the Bread of Life which we this day have spurned. In Jesus' name. Amen," said the head of the house. "Amen," echoed weakly his wife and his daughter.

28

After their first year in Geneva had ended, providence dealt a series of blows to the Calvin family on Canon St. Jean Calvin's political honeymoon was over. The Libertines, those well-to-do citizens who had always hated any effort made to clean up the city, rebelled more openly now. They seized every effort to support any new enemy of Jean Calvin that appeared on the horizon. These Libertines wielded influence with the often indecisive Councils which ruled Geneva.

One defeat to Calvin was the reopening of the taverns. When Jean Calvin first came to the city the infamous Madeleine quarter of the city boasted that one of every third house in the district was a tavern. Sick of the carousing that went on in these places, and after a long, hard-fought battle the Reformer had succeeded in having them closed. Eating and drinking places which replaced the taverns were refined restaurants called abbayes. In these eating places the Bible was always in evidence. Anyone neglecting to bow his head for grace before eating was refused service. After nine in the evening there were no eating places open in the city. This was all changed again and the bawdy all-night taverns flourished in spite of the Reformer's efforts.

Tucked away in these political heartaches came a new personal loss. Pierre Viret's wife died after a short but serious illness. Jean Calvin had written on learning of

Madame Viret's sickness, "Be assured we are as anxious about her, as if she were our own wife or daughter." Now that she was dead, upon Jean Calvin's urgings Pierre, himself, came to be comforted to the home of his dearest friend. Jean Calvin was always at his greatest in these moments of sorrow. Idelette, by comparison, always felt grief deeply but found herself extremely inarticulate when she tried to impart sympathy.

In all these afflictions which followed thick and fast the only rainbow in sight was actually of a negative character. When Pierre Blanchet, chaplain at the plague lazar, died, after twice serving in that pest hole, Jean Calvin again had thrust his own application to serve as plague chaplain on the Little Council. His distress over the death of Pierre Blanchet was augmented by the fact that the brave young minister had served twice with gallantry in that much dreaded post — his second term had resulted because the appointed minister had defaulted and Jean Calvin's own offer to serve had been rejected. Pierre had died, Jean Calvin felt, in his stead. Jean Calvin's present application for the post was no sudden decision on his part. As early as October, 1542, he had written Pierre Viret, "I fear that after him it will be my turn to run the risk: We cannot fail those who need our ministry." Now he fulfilled that pledge.

The Little Council, to Idelette's relief, refused to accept his offer. They took official action, which once and for all, removed this dread from his fearful wife. They stated that Monsieur Calvin was to be exempted from the service because he was needed for the Church.

29

Idelette did not like Antoine's wife. With her usual honesty she faced this fact. It was easier to analyze her own feelings than to trace down her reason for them. For on the surface of things she should have been happy with her brother-in-law's choice. Ann Calvin was always amiable, friendly and helpful with the house duties — whenever she and her husband lived under the Jean Calvin roof. She did nothing to arouse animosity, and for this reason Idelette's own feelings bothered her conscience. She was fair enough to worry that her own attitude lay in no fault in Ann Calvin, but rather in her own self.

She was especially disturbed because she seemed alone in her opinion. Antoine was completely enamoured by his wife. And Jean Calvin, a good judge of character — except for an occasional complaint about Ann's talkativeness — had nothing but words of commendation for her. Even Judith paid Ann compliments in her own way by aping her aunt's dress, her accent and other mannerisms.

Idelette wondered if her feelings were rooted in jealousy. She thought not. She was too secure in the love and affection of her family to resent her beautiful sister-in-law. And yet it was impossible to track down the origin of her distaste. If she were able to place a finger on any special trait that made her uneasy it was a minor vice, namely the softness of Ann Calvin. Totally feminine in personality, Idelette's sister-in-law lacked completely any masculine hardness. That in itself was not necessarily bad, Idelette realized.

115

But she was penetrating enough to sense that in Ann it was not pure femininity, but rather a lack of character. Her sister-in-law was spineless. *Judith,* Idelette reflected, *will be like her if I cannot instill any strength of will into her.* This passion to be liked by everyone was a deadly poison that too often rotted away any integrity. Ann was infected with it. Judith was to a lesser degree.

Whatever her opinion was about Ann Calvin it remained exclusively her own. Idelette with her customary reticence said nothing to anyone — not even her own husband — about her uneasiness. She herself behaved decorously with her sister-in-law and tried hard to suppress her instinctive dislike.

It was a shock for Idelette one day to discover that among Ann Calvin's many admirers was her husband's secretary, Pierre Dagnet. Antoine and his wife were leaving for their country home after one of their frequent visits. Idelette had surprised the secretary standing at the window watching them intently.

"She is so beautiful," said Pierre Dagnet wistfully. "They make such a handsome couple."

Idelette joined him at his place of observation. "They have been very happy together." She forced herself to state that truth.

Pierre Dagnet's look dismayed Idelette. But he said nothing.

"You do not agree with me, Pierre?"

"Monsieur Antoine Calvin is happy. I am not so sure about his wife."

Idelette thought too much of her husband's secretary's judgment to doubt his statement. Like so many physically handicapped people — forced into a role of observer — he was shrewd in his observations. But she was reluctant to gossip about her sister-in-law even with Pierre Dagnet, who had become her friend. She did not press the subject any further. But Idelette, too, was an observer by native disposition, and she decided that she would be alert to see if Pierre Dagnet's suspicions were true.

30

Jean Calvin dipped his pen into the inkwell and wrote in his careful script, "She has a gracious face, and her whole body is marvelously beautiful. My friend Jean Petit says I am completely enamoured by her."

"What are you doing, Father?"

"I am writing a letter, petite, to a dear friend."

"To which dear friend?"

"You must not bother your father," Idelette spoke from her chair by the fire.

"Am I bothering you, Father?"

Monsieur Calvin laughed, picked up Judith, and set her on his knee. "Yes, you are. And you are not to contradict your mother."

Judith sat where she was, picked up a second quill pen, and started to draw pictures.

"To whom are you writing, Jean?" his wife asked.

"I give up," said Monsieur Calvin. "You women have an instinct about romance, and you must probe until you find it. Little women or grown-up little girls, you are all alike."

"You are still leaving my question unanswered."

Jean Calvin threw up his hands in mock horror. "I yield. I am writing Pierre Viret that I have found the perfect wife for him."

Idelette frowned, "His first wife has not been dead very long."

117

"And she was a very good woman and your dear friend. I know. I know. But Pierre has been beside himself since her death. When a man feels sorrow the way he does it is better to waste no time."

"You may be right. My mother would say when a man marries again it is because his first marriage was a good one."

"Your mother was a wise woman."

"Will you then, too, prove your love for me and marry another within three months when I am gone?"

"That is a different matter."

"Why?"

"I am not Pierre Viret. God has created each one of us differently. Each man has his own pattern for grief. As for myself, if God should deal me so severe a blow that you should die before me, I shall not marry another. With you, my dear, I have had enough love to last a lifetime."

"Why is Mother crying?" Judith asked.

"Because I will not marry again if we should lose her."

"That's silly, isn't it?"

"No, on the contrary, I think it is very sweet."

"May I send a kiss in your letter to Monsieur Viret?" Judith questioned.

"Yes. Write a big X here, and then I shall sign my name. There now, the letter is finished."

31

Jean Calvin was unusually glum at the dinner table. Although Idelette noticed it, she waited until Judith had excused herself before she taxed him with his silence.

"I am angry, Idelette," he expostulated.

She shrank back, "At me?"

"No, of course not."

"Has Judith . . . ?"

"No. No. The child's behavior is always above reproach."

"But at the table you scarcely spoke to either of us."

"I am sorry. How like me to take out my anger on the innocent."

"No. How very unlike you. Would you care to discuss it with me, or would you rather not talk?"

"I am angry at indulgent fathers."

"That covers a wide field." Her remark almost brought a smile.

"Specifically I am angry at one indulgent father."

Idelette said nothing more. The priming had been done. The story poured out. It seemed that after all the laborious effort on Jean Calvin's part at matchmaking for his friend Pierre Viret, and when the marriage between the "marvelously beautiful young girl" and the widower minister was about settled, the girl's father had decided he did not want his daughter to go to live so far from home.

"I told him Lausanne is not so far from Geneva," Jean Calvin stormed. "That Pierre was a man of kindness and indulgence, and would let his daughter make frequent visits to her parental home. But these doting fathers! The girl has a chance of a lifetime, an opportunity to marry one of the finest men in the world, and her father cancels everything because of a matter of mileage!"

"And you have wasted so much time and enthusiasm."

"I was not thinking of myself." Jean Calvin smiled ruefully at his wife. "That wasn't very kind, Idelette. But you may be right. Perhaps I am thinking a little of myself. I am indignant, and I do feel a trifle foolish. How I hate to have to write this news to Pierre."

"Shall I write the letter for you?" his wife offered.

"No. It must be written with great tact and sympathy."

"Oh."

"I know very well, Idelette Calvin, that you do not feel unhappy over this development."

"Now you are unkind, Jean. I am unhappy for you; but you are right in this regard, I shall not shed any tears because Pierre Viret must wait a few months longer for a wife."

Scowling at her, Jean Calvin dipped his pen into the inkstand and sweated out his letter of bad news to his friend. It did not help his efforts much to notice that every time he looked at his wife she was biting back a smile.

32

Ann Calvin was not only a vivacious and spicy conversationalist, she was also a good listener. When you were with her you never doubted that you occupied the center of her attention. This was in part her charm — this ability to make the most insecure and insufficient person feel important. She was very popular with the men and women of the congregation of St. Pierre. When her sister-in-law, Idelette Calvin, listened, you always felt it was with reservations, and that she weighed all statements by her inner morality and was apt to make judgments. The less discriminating Ann Calvin was better liked. She could be counted on to lend a sympathetic and uncritical ear to everyone.

Antoine was pleased with his wife's popularity, and Ann Calvin's circle of friends widened. At first she was content with the easy gains she made with the members of good standing in the church of St. Pierre. Restless, finally, she eyed the greener unexplored pastures and going afield began to make conquests among the society group, the Libertines of Geneva.

Antoine frowned when he first learned that his wife was fraternizing with Franchequine, that wayward daughter of the scandalous Francois Favre family. The father of the family had been convicted several times for adultery. One brother, Gaspard, had been in prison for immorality. Franchequine herself had married well, a councilman and captain general of the Geneva militia, but though she was

superficially established with the right people, no one
doubted that she was a true Favre and in her own way a
fiery rebel against all laws of restraint. Although Antoine
was displeased he did nothing definite about this unpleasant
alliance, excusing it on the grounds of Ann's extreme so-
ciability and lack of discernment.

The attraction which drew together Ann Calvin and
Franchequine Perrin, so different in background, lay in a
striking similarity in one regard. Both women were beautiful, and both had learned effectively how to put beauty to
use. Each possessed a certain measure of unscrupulousness.

When these women first met Franchequine Perrin had
arrived at that stage in her character degeneration when it
pleased her to flaunt the breaking of the established laws
of Geneva. It added spice to the game when Franchequine
was able to shock the pretty wife of Antoine Calvin by her
behavior. Ann Calvin was still not so far removed from her
godly background that she could escape being shocked at
Franchequine's code of ethics. She was especially taken
aback by the manner in which her new friend scoffed at the
concept of marital fidelity.

Franchequine found added sport in her baiting of the
wife of Antoine Calvin since at one time she herself had
been interested in the dark, handsome brother of the ruler
of Geneva. It had angered her when she had discovered
that Antoine, like his brother Jean Calvin, possessed an
armored virtue and a refined distaste for women of her
stripe. She who had not been good enough for Monsieur
Antoine Calvin was amused to discover that there was little
morally to choose between her and the pretty woman he
had married. She felt that a lack of courage was all that
kept Ann virtuous. Franchequine maliciously vowed she
would do all she could to stiffen up the spineless Ann Calvin
and drag her downward with her. Then would come her
moment — the day when Antoine saw his wife as she,
Franchequine Perrin, knew her to be.

But Franchequine was clever. She did not introduce

vice to the more delicate Ann Calvin too swiftly. She first seduced Ann Calvin into breaking some of the minor Genevan laws, into perpetrating little acts of mischief. There were many of these restrictions and punishments at which Franchequine especially chafed. Some of these were: curfew at 9:30 P.M.; anyone going out after that time without a lantern was to be imprisoned on bread and water; card playing prohibited and offenders pilloried; dancing banned. Deliberately she set about to teach Ann Calvin to dance.

"You dance very well. You have instinctive rhythm," Franchequine played on the vanity of Ann.

"You really think so?"

"You dance sinfully well!" Franchequine laughed.

"It is such fun to walk to music." Ann shut her eyes as she danced.

"Especially in a man's arms." Franchequine taunted.

"Is it?" Ann asked wistfully. "I have never danced with a man."

"Then why not come with me tomorrow night and see for yourself?"

"Will there be dancing? Dare there be in Geneva?"

"Antoine Lect is marrying off his daughter, and yes, there will be dancing."

"If I only dared. . . ."

Franchequine looked her scorn.

"What would the Council do if they discovered the violation?"

"Nothing."

"Nothing! How can you be so certain, Franchequine?"

"Do you think they would discipline the daughter of Antoine Lect — or the sister-in-law of Jean Calvin?"

"I am not so sure."

"They keep their disciplines for those who have no pious family background. For me, the daughter of a man who fights to keep open the brothels of Geneva, and other such scum, they keep their disciplines."

"No, no!" A latent loyalty forced Ann to protest.

"Monsieur Jean Calvin fears only God. I know he is no respecter of men."

"Monsieur Calvin?" Franchequine sneered and started to sing a ribald song that was popular with the Libertines.

> "Jean Calvin is a snooper.
> His nose is long and thin.
> It got that way, you know, friends,
> By sniffing hard at sin.
>
> "When decent people sleep, friends,
> His nose is to the ground.
> He's tracking down each sinner
> On his Genevan round."

"Don't, Franchequine, please don't!" Ann Calvin stopped her before she reached the more indecent stanzas. "You know you can be disciplined for such disrespect."

"I am not afraid of that Pope."

Ann drew back. "You don't merely dislike Jean Calvin, Franchequine. You hate him," Ann said with feminine insight. "Why?"

For a moment Franchequine paled. Her eyes stared fixedly at her hands. She clenched then opened her fingers. It was a moment before she regained her self control.

"Shall we dance?" Deliberately she ignored the question.

The dancing lesson continued. But Ann Calvin did not exhibit her new skill at the wedding of the daughter of Antoine Lect. For it was that very night that Antoine Calvin decided he had been too lax with his wife and started the new regime by forbidding her to attend the social event.

"Why?" Ann was petulant at his attitude. She was not used to being crossed by the indulgent Antoine.

"Because," explained her husband with patience, "too many people will be in attendance of whom I disapprove."

"And what if I approve of them?"

"I have been meaning to speak of this for some time,

Ann. But I do not trust your judgment. You have not been wise lately in the choice of your friends."

Ann was stung by this fault-finding in her husband — so alien to their relationship. "You have no right to set yourself up in judgment and to select my friends for me."

Antoine was taken aback. He began to realize that he had allowed the matter to slide far too long. "If I must choose your friends for you, I will," he said firmly. "I have left you to your own choices and look at the many strange doors to which you have gone seeking admittance."

"You mean?"

"I mean among other friendships, I want this association between you and Franchequine Perrin to cease."

"You expect me to suddenly stop seeing her."

"You can explain to her my wishes in the matter."

"I am to tell her that my husband forbids me to have any further friendship with her. I shall do no such thing. I am no child to be ordered about, Antoine."

"I only wish you were." His eyes softened.

"And I shall go to the party tonight."

"Ann!" Antoine was very angry now. He grabbed his wife's shoulders roughly. "You shall respect my wishes in this matter."

"Will you lock me in my room?"

Antoine turned on his heel and left.

33

On the day before the wedding of Antoine Lect's daughter, Idelette Calvin went to the market to buy some food. It was a brisk fall day, and she shivered in her light cloak. She had not been feeling well of late. She was often light-headed and she became easily chilled. She chose her vegetables swiftly. She did not like to linger in crowds lately, for the sentiment of many of the Genevan people was now no longer respectful. Passers-by often jeered not only at her husband but also at herself.

As she turned to leave the fruit stall Franchequine Perrin entered. Idelette had to step aside to let her by. Trotting at the Libertine woman's heels was a large fuzzy black poodle. In friendly fashion it stopped and sniffed at Idelette. Her hand dropped to pat the dog when Franchequine whistled and called, "Come, Jean. Jean Calvin! Come here at once!" Idelette cringed at the cruelty of the action. She knew how many of the Libertine families were naming their dogs after her husband to show their disrespect. It seemed so mean, so petty and so childish to resort to such tactics. She should have been able to meet the insult with dignity. But her poise forsook her. Her own weakness of body betrayed her. She could not speak. She was afraid at any moment she would break down and cry. She turned and fled the market place.

She arrived home breathless to find Jean at the door.

He took her basket of purchases from her and chided her for her haste as he walked into the kitchen with her. Unlike his usual habit he lingered in the room and finally sat down in a corner of the large fireplace and rubbed his hands together over the open flame. He stayed and watched her prepare the evening meal.

She felt his eyes on her. It made her uneasy to work under his scrutiny. "What is it, Jean? Is something wrong?"

"Must something be wrong in order for a man to sit in the kitchen with his wife?" he said somewhat tartly.

"Not for a man," she replied with spirit, "but when Jean Calvin leaves his study an hour before the evening meal. . . ." She finished the sentence with a shrug that spoke for her.

"Am I so methodical?"

"When I hear you push back the chair in your study I start to warm the broth on the flames. It will take you exactly four minutes to wash and come down. By that time the pot will be boiling."

"Then I am to be given credit for your excellent broth."

She smiled her slow smile, but did not answer. "And tonight?" he continued.

"Tonight the broth is still cold," she interrupted, "and I am afraid I shall forget to put it on altogether."

She turned to stir the vegetables in the kettle. He started to hum a tune. The spoon clattered to the floor as she whirled around. He saw the look of consternation on her face. "Then you, too, have heard the latest ditty, Idelette."

"Jean, I . . ." She crossed to him and laid one of her slender hands gently across his forehead.

"I had hoped you had not heard it, that you at least would not have to suffer indignity for righteousness' sake." He started to chant, " 'Jean Calvin is a snooper. His nose is long and thin — ' "

She pressed her fingers gently across his lips to shut out the words. He rested his head against her and shut his eyes. "It has never been easy for me to be a reformer,

Idelette. My duties go against my own nature. I wish, how I wish I could shield you from this ridicule which is a necessary part of the unpleasant task that God has laid upon me. If you had not married me . . ."

She laughed. "I love your laugh, Idelette. You should laugh oftener. Am I to blame that there is so little which occasions laughter in your life? If we had stayed in Strasbourg. If — "

Again she laughed. This time she spoke. "Jean, I have never heard you say 'if' so many times before. What is it you once wrote on the subject of divine providence, 'Whatever happens to the believer is permitted and directed by His righteous dispensation.' Institutes 3,234."

He pulled her down upon his lap and ran his fingers through the tiny tight curls which the moist steam from the kettle was making about her face. "You read too many books."

"The broth, Jean!"

"Tonight there will be no broth."

34

Franchequine twisted her heavy black hair around the wire tampons. Ami, her husband, was already in bed asleep. She pouted as she saw his mouth slacken and sag and quiver with every breath. With his mouth closed her husband was passably handsome, but like this — she made a *moue* at the steel mirror she held in her hands. Her own reflection pleased her more. She liked her pert little face, black sparkling eyes which appeared to tilt at the corners, a mouth overlarge but beautifully shaped, and lovely even white teeth which showed at every opportunity. She practiced a smile. How grateful she was to have all her own teeth. So many of her friends had black teeth or some missing. She took a closer look at her own hair — was that a gray one? No, it was just the way the candle light highlighted it. It was lovely hair, glossy and thick, and after sleeping with the tampons it would puff out fashionably.

Antoine Lect's daughter was being married tomorrow. Franchequine had bought a new dress for the occasion. It was daring. She did hope Ami would not be stuffy about it. He was so unpredictable. One moment he stood firmly with the Council upholding their stringent rules. The next moment he would become angry with them and would ridicule them and make sarcastic remarks about Jean Calvin.

The very thought of Jean Calvin brought a frown to Franchequine's face. How she hated that man! Ann Calvin had asked her why. She would tell no one why; but how well she remembered the moment her hate was born. It had started that Sunday in church. Since church attendance was compulsory she together with Ami sat regularly in their places in St. Pierre with the rest of the Genevans — the enthusiastic and the reluctant. Jean Calvin had a commanding presence, and in spite of herself Franchequine usually found she must give the preacher her grudging attention. She had been especially happy that morning, for Ami, the tight-pursed, had given her a lovely ruby ring. She was twisting it on her finger and watching the way it flashed in the reflected glow from the stained glass window, and admiring the way its size set off her own long tapering fingers, when a phrase from the pulpit had crashed through her self-adulation. "The wages of sin is death." As she clenched her hands together she heard the minister continue with his disagreeable picture of the flower which fadeth. Words of death and decay, forbidding words, destroyed her peace of mind. Her imagination played a trick on her. Even as she admired her rosy-tipped fingers some strange reflected light from the window made it appear that before her eyes the flesh melted away from her hands, and she found herself staring at the bony skeleton of fingers, her own fingers. The image had been so real that she had nearly fainted.

Franchequine Perrin was not easily frightened. She had never forgiven Jean Calvin for that moment. She, who deliberately had placed thoughts of death and mortality behind her, had had to sit and face that awesome possibility that one day she Franchequine Perrin would die. She would be nothing but a heap of bones and rotted flesh. It was a horror she could never escape. Unless she kept her mind full of trifles the memory of that moment would rise to torment her. Even now her beautiful mirror played tricks on her. Sockets appeared instead of eyes. How she hated Jean Calvin. How dared he make the thoughtless think? It was sinful to cause the terror and unhappiness which he was doing. Life was for the living. One should banish all hateful thoughts of death. Defiantly she began to hum the taunting song, "Jean Calvin is a snooper." She laughed maliciously as she thought of her meeting with Madame Calvin in the grocery store. That poor woman had the spirit of a frightened rabbit. How she detested spirit-less women. The Calvin men seemed destined to mate them. Ann Calvin was a mouse. She was worse than Idelette. She had neither the spunk to be good nor bad. She hummed louder. Now Ami stirred on his bed, awakened and said disagreeably, "Come to bed, Franchequine, and stop that stupid humming."

Franchequine was ready with a tart reply when she remembered the dress she wanted to wear to the wedding the next day. It was daring. It would be just as well to have Ami in a good humor tomorrow.

"Coming, dear," she said in her sweetest tone, and blew out the candle.

35

The wedding of Antoine Lect's daughter, by which so many lives were altered, was a grand affair. Musicians had been hired in flagrant violation of Genevan laws, and dancing was held. Carriages drove up endlessly to the large brick house of Antoine Lect and discharged many of the best families of the city.

The bride was plain enough, somewhat plump, a straw blonde with a vacuous smile. But what she lacked in beauty was compensated for by a rich dowry, and many a Genevan gentleman cast envious glances at the bridegroom fortunate enough to become a part of the Lect family.

The bride was quite eclipsed in magnificence by Franchequine Perrin who was scandalously dressed in red velvet. The vivacious Madame Perrin had tightened her waistline with wooden splints and she had worn a farthingale to give the required fashionable width to her hips. Her frock fell in soft big flute-like folds over a stiffened pad stretched upon a wire frame, and swayed to and fro as she danced. She had worn a stiff high stand-up collar of white, the front was open, and the bodice cut so low it offended the taste of even some of the loose-living Libertines.

Animated and flirtatious, she dominated the scene. She danced every dance, and more with her host than even the more liberal Genevans deemed proper. Ami, her husband, however, mellowed by the food and drink, overlooked his wife's behavior. He himself was engrossed in trying to buy some property which he had been wanting for months, and the evening's cultivation of the owner seemed to guarantee success.

As he and Franchequine rode home in the dawn hours, they both gloated silently in the triumphs of the evening. It was not until morning that the blow fell. Both received a summons to appear before the Consistory for violation of the Genevan law prohibiting dancing.

Most of the guests, including the host, apologized immediately and were forgiven. But for once the Perrin house stood together. Ami's pride would not permit him to submit to the summons. Franchequine was adamant in her refusal, and punctuated her own attitude with profanity. How dared that swine Jean Calvin touch her now that she was the wife of Ami Perrin! As Franchequine Favre she had no protection. But her husband Ami was one of the men who had gone to Strasbourg to recall that little pope back to Geneva. She raved and ranted. She showed herself a perfect example of Jean Calvin's own comment, "Bad people are like toads who eject venom when pricked."

Months dragged on. Then Ami, with his customary vacillation, gave in. Franchequine was furious at his betrayal. She moved out of her own home and back to stay with her father. All the members who had attended the wedding had taken their censure but not she. "The weaklings. Let them cringe," she stormed. "The cowards. That pig-headed Council will never crush me." Once before in one of her rages she had tried to ride down a preacher that had dared censure her. Jean Calvin had better beware.

It was Ann Calvin, that spiritless woman, who was ironically the instrument which finally broke her spirit. In a mistaken feeling of loyalty Ann had slipped into the Favre house to warn Franchequine that she must flee for she was to be arrested. Franchequine had been dragged to prison once before. Although the matron had not dared to hold her, it was an experience Franchequine had no ambition to repeat. Bread and water were not for her. Shrewdly she realized that Ann's source of information must have been the top man of the city. Although Franchequine was no coward, she was also no fool. With no Ami to stand back of her, flight seemed the only solution. Gathering together what jewels and money she could, she fled Geneva.

She cursed Jean Calvin. She cursed the Council as a whole and each member individually. She cursed her husband. But most of all she cursed herself for her stubborn folly. She fled by boat across Lake Leman. She, Franchequine Perrin, was banishing herself from Geneva. She knew she had lost, at least temporarily. What lay ahead? Her father would help her but in some strange city. Geneva, the city she loved, was no longer home. She looked back at her city. Massive Saint Pierre towered above the brick houses of the Madeleine sector. She spat in the water. As she spat her face reflected in the water distorted itself, and once again she saw the spectre of death. Franchequine Perrin shuddered. Her father could help her start life someplace else. But it would only postpone the day, the day that would always come, the day she could not escape, the day of the death of Franchequine Perrin. And her soul? What of her soul? Did she have an immortal soul?

One of the boatmen started to hum a tune. It was an attempt to show his sympathy for the wickedness of Franchequine. "Jean Calvin is a snooper." Franchequine laughed uproariously and joined in singing all the ribald verses. She had been saved by a song. Saved from being saved! For a moment she, Franchequine Perrin, had almost turned back.

36

Another of the guests whose life changed radically after the wedding of the daughter of Antoine Lect was Ann Calvin. She had attended the affair in spite of her husband's prohibitions. But she had not joined in the dancing, her courage failing her. That much at least her husband's firmness had accomplished. But it was cold comfort to Antoine, for he was not aware that his wife had learned the art of dancing. He felt, therefore, when the wrath of the Little Council descended on the dancing guests and Ann escaped censure it was due to a virtue which on her part consisted in not sinning for lack of the talent to sin. Although Ann escaped the Genevan discipline, her flaunting of her husband's orders caused an inevitable rift between them.

Temporarily, however, things were better. Frightened by her experience, a chastened Ann avoided keeping open company with the Libertines. Her weakness of disposition would have made her an easy target for a return to virtue if Antoine had cared to make the effort. But he was not a man who could forgive betrayal easily. Ann's own moral fiber was not strong enough to lead to any genuinely permanent repentance. But she was also too weak to flaunt her continued disobedience. Outwardly at least there was no break in the Antoine Calvin household. Ann became more careful in her social life. To avoid any further open clashes and precipitate marital conflict she arranged her outings. She began to take frequent walks with young Judith, and the wise child was quickly aware that she was being used by her aunt to cloak unapproved pastimes.

Antoine was satisfied that his wife stayed at home or walked with the child. Idelette was uneasy but she counted on Ann's softness to avoid further trouble and was not suspicious of Ann's double life. Judith alone knew.

Judith knew her aunt walked with strange men, played cards with Libertine groups while she sat solemnly by and feasted on bon-bons. But Judith did not tell. In a strange way Judith was fascinated by her new role of confidante. Ann never asked for the child's silence; she knew Judith's secretive disposition and extreme loyalty to her were on her side, and she banked on it.

The child was too young to have placed on her shoulders the burden of deceit. She loved her pretty aunt. Sin, which she had always been taught to shun, now appeared in a new light — an enticing one. Thus the poison spread from Franchequine Perrin to Ann Calvin to the child of Idelette Calvin. And the cancer grew within the body of Jean Calvin's own family and lay undiscovered until it was too late.

As time passed Ann Calvin continued to flirt with sin. However, she always managed to draw back in time to avoid any deep disaster. She was not so happy in her new life as she led her niece Judith to believe. She craved love and admiration from one and all. Antoine's coldness unnerved her. She knew that with one foolish stroke she had amputated her hold on him. Her husband was polite — even affectionate at times, but no longer devoted. This failure frightened her. Forced by the new Antoine to limited outings, she had to stay more at home and thus unexpectedly found a source of sympathy in the secretary of Jean Calvin, Pierre Dagnet.

Pierre Dagnet did not censure her. He seemed to understand her limitations and accept her in spite of them. He made no demands of her that she could not keep. This was a new type of conquest for her. To foster all former relationships her weapon had been deceit. Her conquests had not ever truly known her. Pierre Dagnet knew her for what she was and loved her.

Ann Calvin was sure of this fact. What intelligence she lacked in other areas amounted to genius when it came to affairs of the heart. Even as she became more and more certain that the rift between Antoine and herself was permanent, she was equally sure that Pierre Dagnet was her devoted slave. It was the salve she needed; and with her usual lack of heart she did not hesitate to make use of the man's devotion.

The excursions with Judith became less frequent. Ann had found, in her own easy-going manner, a pleasant safer pastime more at hand, one she could enjoy with less danger and effort. Again she played with sin. Pierre Dagnet, unlike the woman he loved, had a bad conscience over the relationship. But with bitter irony he realized that the reason the situation between himself and the wife of Antoine Calvin did not erupt into adultery was not so much his torments of conscience, but the lack of courage on the part of the woman he loved.

37

The name of Michael Servetus was often heard in the Calvin household. In fact it had its frequent place in the conversational topics starting from the day a copy of the *Restitutes* had arrived by post for Jean Calvin. The Reformer opened this subject of Michael Servetus by saying that the book was the most damnable he had ever read.

"May I read it, Jean?" asked Idelette.

He gave it reluctantly to her. "Take it. I did not realize I had said anything to recommend it to your attention. But read it. We shall discuss it together when you have finished. You should be informed about its content. But God knows I feel as if I were handing you an adder."

Idelette took the manuscript and painstakingly worked through it. When she had finished she went in to the study to discuss it with her husband.

"You have read it?"

"Yes."

"Did you understand what you read?"

"Not much," she replied honestly.

Calvin smiled.

"That pleases you?"

"I have no desire that Monsieur Michel de Villeneuve speak with the gift of clarity."

"Jean, did you say Michel de Villeneuve?"

"Yes. Michael Servetus and Michel de Villeneuve are

138

one and the same. To escape death from the Spanish Inquisition Servetus is living under an assumed name near
the city of Lyons, France."

"I seem to have heard the name de Villeneuve somewhere."

"Certainly not from me, and not in Geneva."

"Not in Geneva." Idelette spoke thoughtfully. "I know
now. I remember. The driver spoke his name. Jean, it was
he who befriended me on the way to Strasbourg and left
without identifying himself."

"Then I am in his debt." Jean looked affectionately
at his wife.

"Jean, he spoke so well of you. He said he had read
your books."

"He is a Spaniard, a born gallant. He would not stoop
to offend a lady by speaking ill of her husband. He has
read my *Institutes*. This is what he thinks of my work." He
handed Idelette a copy of the *Institutes* which he had
mailed to Michael Servetus. Idelette frowned as she read
the insulting comments Michael Servetus had made on the
margins before he had returned the work.

"We have had a long correspondence, Idelette. Here, if
you wish, read his last letter to me."

Idelette took the letter and read aloud in a halting
voice. "False are all the invisible Gods of the Trinitarians,
as false as the gods of the Babylonians."

"See here," Calvin pointed to a passage, "he refers to
the Trinity as a three-headed Cerberus."

Idelette shivered at the words. "Can no one show him
the error in his thoughts? I wish, someday, Jean, you could
speak with him."

"I have never had the opportunity, Idelette. Once,
years ago in Paris, when we were both young and both in
jeopardy of our lives, he arranged an appointment with me.
I kept it, but fruitlessly. He never appeared. I do not know
why. I have always regretted this. But others have worked
with him. Even Okolampad, the great Reformer of Basel,

tried to convert him by friendly influence and conversation, and finally wrote to his friend Zwingli about him, 'He is so proud, presumptuous and quarrelsome that it is all to no purpose.' When these others have failed, would not my attempts be feeble and futile by comparison?"

"But these others are not logicians. You both are. You both started out to study law. He seemed to me to have such an alert mind."

"And he was very kind to you. I shall remember that, Idelette. I promise you, if I ever meet him, I shall do all I can to turn him to worship the living and the true God. I can only hope the meeting will never occur in Geneva. I have been becoming increasingly distressed at his teachings. If I should fail to turn him from his path of sowing wicked philosophies there would be no alternative for me but to condemn him to death for his blasphemies against the Lord, my God. Meanwhile, this is the most appropriate place for his writings."

He took the manuscript from her hands and placed it on the crackling logs in his fireplace. And the book burned. It was only a book yet Idelette felt it was a solemn, symbolic occasion. It was as if in his own mind Monsieur Calvin had reached a decision on the matter of Michael Servetus.

38

Monsieur Calvin's study in the home on Canon St. was sparsely furnished. In it he had a table and bench for himself, one large bookcase, and a small stepladder on which he climbed to reach the higher shelves. There was no chair nor sofa, only one other bench for visitors.

But the bareness within was greatly compensated for by the splendor of the view without. From his window Monsieur Calvin could see to the left the Jura Mountains; to the right the major range of the Alps; and always down below the deep blue Lake Leman. There were times when Jean Calvin felt inspired by the stupendous grandeur of the mountains. Other days his heart was gladdened by the tranquility of the lake. Always above was the ever present inspiration of the sky.

Some of Jean Calvin's happiest moments were spent within this bare room. His privacy within its walls was always respected. The closing of the study door in the Calvin household was sufficient notification that disorder and disturbance be curbed. His family knew that when he withdrew within his cloister that in reality he was in a different world. He was with his God.

Sometimes Idelette would pause from the rush of her daily tasks, and, when her husband was absent, would slip into the room by herself. It was always in perfect order, although this was one room she never dusted. The orderliness of her husband's mind extended into everything with which he came in contact. Everything was in its place. Each book had its groove. He dusted the room himself, handling each book as a friend. The room seemed to absorb his personality. It seemed to breathe out order, austerity and peace.

Jean Calvin found his wife in the study one day. She had drawn the bench over to the window and was sitting looking out at the mountains. She rose as he entered, but he pushed her down again, and sat beside her.

"The view is lovelier than the one we had in Strasbourg," he said.

"Much grander, Jean. But," she said wistfully, "I liked looking down from our window at the Petite Eglise."

"The way of women," he teased. "Always longing for what is past. I secure a bigger and better house with a garden. And with nostalgia you remember a house whose shutters were awry, whose roof leaked and whose steps were hazardous — "

"But where we had peace," she finished for him.

He put an arm gently about her tiny waist. She rested her head on his shoulder. "Need I remind you that peace is within? Look out there," he said, changing the subject. "See the clouds above the mountains. Snow clouds. Shall we sit inside our shelter and watch the storm break, you and I, together?"

"At least it will be a novelty not to have it breaking over our heads."

"Idelette, Idelette," he chided gently. "Is the fight, then, too much for you?" He looked with anxious eyes at her pale face.

"I am sorry, Jean. The fight seems too formidable, today. But tomorrow will bring new strength."

The sky became very dark. Suddenly those soft delicate flakes began to fall. Monsieur and Madame Calvin sat in silence and watched the hillside turn white before their eyes. The snow would not remain long on the ground. It would melt before morning, but far away on the mountains it would remain the winter long.

"This storm will be good for our garden," said Monsieur Calvin.

"Yes, storms are good for us," replied his wife.

Jean Calvin was content. Idelette was herself again.

39

Death was no stranger to Idelette. But although it had brushed her skirts many times during her lifetime, still, like most mortals she had subconsciously assumed it was something that would bypass her. But as she dragged her weary body around doing her daily tasks, tasks which formerly had been accomplished with ease and pleasure, she could no longer assume that this weakness, too, would pass. Even the coming of spring brought no resurgence of strength. Her sense of immortality in this life deserted her.

An unusually severe spasm of coughing sent her reeling outdoors for a breath of air. Gratefully she rested on the iron bench, pressing her hands tightly over her aching temples. There could no longer be any doubt in her mind. She had started to walk through the Valley of the Shadow of Death.

"Oh, my God," she prayed in agony. "Do not take me now. A year. Grant me but another year."

She could not die now. Never had life been harder for the Calvins. The Libertines were hounding the Reformer constantly with large and petty issues. She no longer enjoyed the walk to the common fountain to draw water and talk to neighbors. It was impossible anywhere to escape the jeering taunts of the women. Franchequine had fled Geneva, but other women took up her cry calling their dogs, "Jean, Jean Calvin! Here's a nice juicy bone!" Another year. Surely by then justice would triumph, and she could go tranquilly home to God. How could God take her now when Jean most sorely needed her love and affection? She must be a buffer for him against the angry shouts of the multitudes who opposed most of his reforms purely for self-interest. There were men, like Pierre Ameaux, whose living had been making gambling cards who hated Jean Calvin for the laws introduced against gambling. Naturally this edict had wreaked havoc with his business. There were others whose income had come from the infamous houses of prostitution who resented their closing and the subsequent curtailment of income. And there were some others, irritated by the strict Genevan laws, who permitted themselves to be used by these more wicked people and joined in the vocal opposition of Jean Calvin. This was no time to die.

The handkerchief she pressed to her mouth was red with blood. In all her religious life Idelette had never felt such rebellion of soul. How horrified Jean would be if he knew to what a state her love for him had brought her. Here she was, Idelette the meek, challenging a plan of the Almighty. She was too well tutored in the theology of her husband to resist long. Her unexpected rebellion died almost at the moment of birth. She wept. How should she pray? It seemed no longer right to pray for life. What was it her husband had said of prayer? Once, long ago, his words had helped her. Now under such different circumstances she clung to the comfort they gave.

"But when we are convinced that God must pass by some need, and that the will of God is known to us, then it is no longer a matter of making of Him another request, unless that He may strengthen us in power and in invincible constancy, and that we may make no complaint, or that we may not be carried away by our affections; but that we may go with a ready courage through everything to which He calls us." Idelette repeated the last phrase to herself. "That we may not be carried away by our affections; but that we may go with a ready courage through everything to which He calls us."

A ready courage. "Oh, Almighty God," she prayed, "grant me a ready courage." There was one last gift she could give her husband. She could die well. She had heard saints of God on their deathbeds, tortured with death agonies, augment the bereavement of their loved ones by a cowardly homegoing. When her moment came, and her body and soul were torn apart — in that moment of anguish, with God's help, she pledged to make her death a glorious one. In this way she could comfort even beyond the grave.

Idelette's prayers for herself changed after her moment with God in the garden. She no longer prayed for life. She prayed, instead, that God strengthen her in "power and invincible constancy." And she prepared her soul for death. As she did so, comfort came. Her concern for those she must leave behind was lessened, as once again God chose to give her comfort through the words of her husband, "The grace of the Lord, which inhabits my house, will not leave it desolate."

I must die, thought the dying woman. *But how glorious, God abides. He will not leave my home desolate.*

40

Pierre Viret had his child. The cradle would at last be used. As Idelette held the newborn in her arms she felt a wave of melancholy sadness for Chou Chou who never bore Pierre a living child, for herself who had lost her little Jacques. But it was hard to remain sad when she cradled in her arms a new life, a lovely little girl who looked like a solemn owl, with a round head and big button eyes. Idelette looked at the proud mother. Pierre, unaided, had done well in his second wife. His loveliness of spirit seemed to capture people of like mind and fetter them to him.

Idelette's warm heart went out to the second Madame Viret. She was so young, yet so understanding. The difference in age and her close friendship with the first Madame Viret were not obstacles in this new relationship. It was Idelette that Sebastienne Viret had wanted to stay with her for this birth of her first child. And although she was weak and sick Idelette did not refuse to come. This moment of birth was her reward.

Idelette rubbed oil on the body of the newborn baby and wrapped the infant snugly in swaddling cloth and brought it to the mother. "You have a solemn little woman."

Madame Viret held the baby close to her. "Thank you, Idelette, for coming and staying with me. Your presence banishes all pain and fear of death."

Idelette smiled sadly.

Sebastienne Viret looked searchingly at her friend. "You suffer much?"

"The pain never leaves me now."

"Can Doctor Textor do nothing for you?"

"He has already done much. But the Great Physician has other plans."

"No, Idelette. Do not say that."

"My friend, one learns the longer one lives that life and death are His to give and His to withhold. We who accept the one from his hands, should we not equally accept the other?"

"Does Jean know?"

Pain was reflected on Idelette's features. "He has so much about which to grieve at present. When it is necessary we shall speak of it together. I could not burden him yet."

"Charles? What of your son? Will you send for him now?" The new mother held her newborn close.

Idelette's face brightened at the mention of her son. "It is not good for the young to be exposed to too much grief. Ever since I have known how things are with me, I have not wanted Charles near me. He has suffered. I want to spare him. I do not want him to see me die."

"And Judith, does she know?"

A spasm of pain crossed Idelette's face. "I never know what Judith knows or thinks. But this is no time, my friend, to speak of death. A child is born today. This is a day for rejoicing. Another Viret. A solemn little baby. If one may judge by appearances she will be a lady Solomon."

The ten days Idelette spent caring for Madame Viret and the new baby in Lausanne were happy ones. Idelette, relieved from the pretense of health she practised vigorously at home, was comforted with friends who knew she was dying. She had time, now, time and solitude to cultivate the courage she desired.

On her return to Geneva Jean noticed a new strength in his wife. And because he wished it so much, he attributed it to increased health and vitality and his spirits soared. As her body weakened Idelette found her spirit strengthened. The shadows were gone. The sun, it seemed to her, shone brighter than ever before, lighting her pathway to Eternal Day.

41

It seemed as if the winter of 1549 would never end. Idelette kept moving around the house with pure effort of will. Even the short walk to St. Pierre's had become too difficult for her.

Antoine's wife Ann came more frequently now to help with the work. And she and Judith took care of most of the necessities of the household. Idelette found it hard to relinquish these daily tasks which seemed her last tie with earth. She knew now that when she was gone Monsieur Calvin's brother and his wife would make their home at Canon St. She was happy that her husband and child would not suffer any lack of material comfort; but she was still uneasy about the character of Ann Calvin.

Certain rumors about her sister-in-law began at last to penetrate even the thick walls of the Calvin home, which did not welcome gossip. Idelette felt her approaching death gave her a certain liberty of speech; and one day, casting aside her customary reluctance to interfere in another's life, she taxed Ann with her conduct.

"Ann, is it true that you were out riding Monday last with Monsieur Dubonnet?"

"Yes. It is true." Ann tossed her head defiantly.

"Does Antoine know?"

"Why should he?"

"You know his wishes in such matters."

"You mean he limits my friendships. He is absurdly jealous."

"A man sure of the affection of his wife is seldom jealous."

"What should I do? Sit at home all day?" Ann was petulant.

"Other women do. They find sufficiency in a husband's love."

"I do not have a husband's love."

"Ann! Antoine is devoted to you."

Ann started to cry. "Not any more. Not since the wedding of Antoine Lect's daughter. I hear nothing now but rantings from him."

"Your continued bad behavior may merit them." Idelette was sharp. Then seeing the tearful face she continued more gently. "Forgive my interference, but I am concerned for your happiness. Can you not try, Ann, to make your marriage a success?"

"You call it a failure?"

"Are you happy the way you are living?"

"Yes," said Ann defiantly.

"Is Antoine happy?"

"No." Ann replied reluctantly. "But why do you scold me? Why am I responsible? Why should Antoine be allowed to behave toward me as if I were a leper?"

"Oh, Ann, Ann! It would be so easy for you to charm him to yourself again. If you would only try."

"Idelette. Please understand. For you it is easy to find complete happiness within your walls with one man. I would be bored with your life. I want more freedom of movement. I must have it. I need friends, many friends. If you would help Antoine and me, please urge him to unshackle me. Don't let him force me to cut out of my life the company of men who give me back my self-esteem. Make him give me back my friends."

"And in these friendships has there ever been any betrayal of your vows to Antoine?"

"No, Idelette, never. Life is so short. Let me be gay."

Sadness and a new tenderness for Ann flooded Idelette. How trite but how true. Life is short. Facing death as she was, she felt sympathy for her sister-in-law. Antoine may have been too stern. He had been right to be angry at Ann's cultivation of the Libertines. But after years of indulging his pretty wife this complete turnabout did not seem wise.

"I shall speak to Antoine, if you wish. He loves you, Ann, very much. I know he does. Don't ever betray that love."

Ann Calvin, who lived for the moment, was delighted with Idelette's support. Antoine, she knew, would not refuse the wise Idelette. Impulsively she embraced her sister-in-law.

Idelette returned the embrace. "You have been so good to me during my illness, Ann — so very helpful. When I am gone — "

"Idelette, what are you saying? You must not speak so. I will not listen. You will soon be well and strong again."

There was so much Idelette wanted to say, so many plans for the future when she was gone that she would have liked to have talked over with Ann. But her sister-in-law was not one who would accept an unpleasant fact. There was no use in preparing her for what lay ahead. It was foolish to expect more from a person than that person had to give. Seeing the anxious eyes fastened on her, she smiled, "Yes, I shall soon be well and strong again." Ann was reassured. She had not, as Idelette had expected, sensed the hidden meaning.

42

Antoine and Ann were feted by Idelette with a farewell meal. Idelette had a sudden upsurge of strength and felt better than she had for some time. She insisted on managing everything. It was a happy family table. Jean was always glad when his brother and wife were under his roof. He was very fond of Antoine; and this was to be a dinner in honor of an occasion, for Antoine and his wife Ann were planning a trip to Bale. Idelette sensed that the journey was a result of her own talk with her brother-in-law about his domestic troubles, an effort on his part to regain some sort of stable family life. Although Antoine showed no special animation at the meal, Ann was unusually gay and excited over the prospect of an unexpected change of scene. Only Judith looked downcast. She was fond of her vivacious aunt, and she was unhappy at the thought of her prolonged absence.

Noticing it, and flattered by her niece's feelings, Ann asked her, "You will miss your aunt and uncle, Petite?"

"Very much," the young girl replied.

"Then why not come too?"

At the unexpected invitation, Antoine was taken aback, but his brother Jean was irritated, "She cannot go. She is needed at home."

Jean had been pleased over the apparent reconciliation of his brother and sister-in-law and had felt the trip a good idea. But he had some selfish misgivings, realizing that once again much of the work that Idelette had reluctantly yielded to her sister-in-law would now be back on her fragile shoulders. Although Idelette seemed improved, her persistent cough and loss of weight worried him. It was of course unthinkable to him that Idelette should lose not only what help Ann Calvin had been able to give, but also at this time the support of her daughter.

"I can get along without Judith," Idelette said quietly. "Madame Frachebourg can come in and care for us. It would be such a lovely experience for the child. A chance like this may not come her way again."

"Oh, Mama, could I really go along?" It seemed unbelievably wonderful to the young girl.

"Are you sure you want her with you?" Idelette turned to Antoine. But it was Ann who answered, "Yes, do let her come. I plan to shop and she will be such company for me."

Antoine, seeing the eagerness in the child's eyes and the affection in Idelette's, yielded with his usual charm, "By all means, send her, Idelette, or I shall have to accompany Ann shopping. Spare me, please!"

Jean still demurred, but found himself out-talked and finally gave his permission. After the early departure of the guests he found himself entering into the spirit of the occasion and gave his advice, frequently unasked, as to what wardrobe Judith should take with her. The small talk, quite unlike the Calvin routine, continued late into the night.

Judith's face was more animated than Jean had ever seen it. "You are happy to leave us, my daughter?" He chided her affectionately.

She came and sat on the arm of his chair. "No, I am very sad to leave you. But I am happy to go."

Idelette smiled. The child had an intuition for saying what would please.

"We shall miss you," Jean said simply, kissing his daughter.

Idelette did not speak and kept her hands busy with the packing to avoid any demonstrations on her part.

"I shall only be away two months, father — not forever," Judith teased him.

"Not forever," echoed Idelette to herself. But she wondered, as with tender hands she folded each garment, if this were the last act of love she would be able to do for her child. For in spite of her new strength she sensed life slipping away from her grasp. It was one reason why she was eager to have Judith in Bale. She did not want the child to see her walk to the gates of the valley of the shadow. She would spare her this sorrow if it were at all possible.

Idelette had no parting message for Judith. All the child's life she had tried to teach her how to walk on the straight and narrow way. Anything she said now would merely be repetitious. And as Judith climbed into the carriage to start on her journey, it was her father who gave her parting admonitions, and it was her father's face that pressed against the window, anxious and tearful. Her mother's face looked to her child as it always had, calm and beautifully serene.

"We shall miss her very much," said Jean as they watched the carriage disappear.

"Yes, we shall."

"It will be only a few months and we shall see her again."

"She will be back very soon." Jean did not notice the evasive answer. Idelette could not bring herself to wipe away the happiness Jean was enjoying in her newfound strength. And when she wept, he felt it was only a normal reaction to being separated temporarily from her daughter.

43

In the end it was not necessary for Idelette to tell her
bad news to Jean. She saw that he knew. And she was
spared this sorrow. All winter long his letters to Pierre
Viret had been full of hope. "Today Idelette is better. The
color is back in her cheeks." Then as time went on, "She is
suffering less today. We are again hopeful." But in March,
shortly after Antoine and Ann Calvin had gone to Bale
with Judith, Idelette's body refused to respond any longer
to her strong will, and she took permanently to her bed.

As she lay in bed Idelette felt only an infinite weari-
ness, and she began to long for the cessation of pain. She
knew that "to be absent from the body was to be present
with the Lord." It was no longer a vague pious quotation
from the Bible, it had become the great reality in life. The
children, even Jean himself, faded into unreality when she
thought of eternity with God.

Jean tiptoed into the sickroom. For a moment he
thought Idelette slept. Then she turned her large eyes
toward him. He came and sat silently beside her. There
was no longer any optimistic pretense between them. They
spoke of her approaching death with a simple matter-of-
factness. Only one subject Idelette never touched, and it
bothered Jean. For he knew with what concern Idelette had
watched over her children in life. Now she did not mention

them. So of his own accord he assured her how tenderly he would care for them.

Her reply was simply, "I have already commended them to God."

He was taken aback, "That does not mean, my dearest, that I have no duty toward them."

Her lips parted in a feeble smile, "I know that you, Jean Calvin, will not neglect those who you know to be commended to God." Then her face grew solemn and a spasm of pain crossed it. It was almost as if in the moment of her death, vision had been given her, a glimpse of what was to come, of the deep wound that one of her own blood would give him in later years. And prophetically she spoke words of comfort to heal a wound which had not yet been dealt.

"The important thing, Jean, is that my children live a pious and godly life. My husband," she laid her soft hand across his cheek, "does not need to be urged to instruct them in a chaste, disciplined life and in the fear of God. If they are pious, I have confidence that spontaneously you will serve them as a father. So I need ask nothing of you. For if they are unworthy I would not ask your favor for them."

And then they spoke of other things — of Pierre Viret, his new wife and infant, of the latest news from Antoine, Ann and Judith. Madame Frachebourg brought in some broth. Her presence was comforting. After drinking the soup Idelette was sleepy again and dozed. And so it continued for several days, this half sleep, this half waking.

Jean Calvin went his rounds dutifully. In addition to his gruelling schedule of preaching daily each alternate week, he continued with his theology class which met three days a week. He attended the weekly meetings of his consistory. He missed none of his obligations. Every possible free waking moment he spent with Idelette.

He was with her when she died. She became suddenly alert and shook herself loose from the lethargic borderland in which she had been living. Jean had been reading to her in the gospel of Matthew, "And the stone had been rolled away from the door. . . ." She raised herself slightly on the pillow and lapsing into the soft speech of her childhood she said in a strong voice, "O wonderful resurrection! Oh God of Abraham, and all our Fathers. Oh hope of all believers since the beginning of the world. On You I hope."

Her voice sank to a whisper, and turning to Jean, she pleaded, "Oh, let us pray. Pray, pray all. Pray also for me."

They were her last words. She died before his prayer was finished. Even as he prayed, he felt her hand, which had been clenched tightly over his own, unclasp. The silver cord was loosed; the pitcher broken at the fountain. For a moment his voice faltered. Then summoning every effort of his tremendous will he changed his prayer of intercession to one of committal; and he committed the soul of his wife into the hands of his Almighty God.

The others in the room remained silent in grief. Only Madame Frachebourg sobbed unrestrainedly. Jean rose slowly to his feet and stumbled into his study and shut the door.

POSTLUDE

And the threads unravelled. The Libertines, who had so threatened the pattern of Idelette's day, gave up at last. Franchequine Perrin, who had finally returned to Geneva to her vacillating spouse, had been with him a party to one final act of wickedness. Ami, together with other prominent Libertines, fostered a hate riot, the object the French refugees in Geneva. The plan was to kill all the French they could find. Ami and his wife plied wine and food into all the loafers and rowdies they could scum off the streets and sent them out to do their killing.

They overdid their work of encouragement. Their agents were too drunk to do much harm and thus the plot boomeranged on the head of the plotters. Seven leaders of the Libertine atrocity were executed. Once again Franchequine, this time accompanied by her husband, escaped death by flight. Geneva had seen the last of the Perrins. Calvin's reign of peace was restored. Geneva became a city of God.

All God's enemies were punished. One other, Michael Servetus, with courage and a generous sprinkling of foolhardiness, set foot in Geneva. He knew when he came that in that city heresy was punishable by death. He also was quite aware that in Geneva heresy was well defined and just where his views fit in the Geneva classification. But having escaped the fires of the Inquisition, and having been burnt only in effigy by the Church of Rome, with a touch of bravado he entered Geneva. He had friends on the Little Council, and it was on them he counted. They failed to save him.

Jean Calvin, true to his promise to Idelette, visited Michael Servetus in jail and did his utmost to convert him. He failed. These were days when execution itself was not enough. It was a time when a man could be drawn, quartered, burned with a slow or fast flame, depending upon the heinousness of the crime. Calvin wishing to spare Servetus a slow death, pleaded with the Council for a quick execution by the sword. When this failed it was his voice which carried the point that the fire be a fast flame.

During these days, Jean wrote to his good friend, Guillaume Farel, about Michael Servetus, "I think he will be condemned to die; but I wish that which is horrible in the punishment may be spared him." Servetus was granted a quick death.

Although victorious politically, Jean Calvin was struck repeatedly by personal tragedy. After flirting years with sin, Ann Calvin stepped over the line of demarcation and was divorced for adultery by her husband Antoine. The corespondent was Pierre Dagnet, the hunchback.

Judith was married docilely to a good man of her father's choice. Guillaume Farel wrote a note of congratulation to his friend about the girl of whom he, too, was very fond, "I congratulate her and because of her, her husband."

Geneva was aghast when seven years later the stepdaughter of Jean, Judith, had to be banished for adultery. The laws of Calvin knew no exceptions to the rule. Her father, who had always loved her, was crushed by her sin.

On May 27, 1564, at 8:00 P.M. Jean Calvin died. Antoine wrote for him his last letter to his friend through the years, Guillaume Farel, urging him not to come to his bedside. He wrote as was dictated, "I am unwilling that you weary yourself for my sake, for I draw breath with difficulty and constantly await its failing me. It is enough that I live and die unto Christ." His stubborn friend ignored the plea and walked to and from Neuchatel to be with the dying man.

In accordance with the Genevan ordinances, at death

Jean Calvin's body was wrapped in a shroud, encased in a plain wooden coffin, and buried somewhere in the cemetery of Plain Palais. By his request there was no marker to indicate the place. It was just another mound, like those of his wife and baby son.

Jean Calvin's life had had moments of great joy and grief. And for eight years these vicissitudes had been shared by Idelette, his wife.

Many people, since his time, have tried to evaluate the genius of Jean Calvin. Williston Walker said of him, "He sacrificed ease, scholarly honors and personal inclination to what he deemed the imperative voice of God."

His contemporary, Pope Pius IV, commented, "That which made the strength of that heretic, was that money was nothing to him."

Bancroft, the American historian, paid tribute in these words, "He who does not honor the memory and influence of Calvin, betrays his ignorance of the origin of American liberty."

We read in Hastings' Encyclopedia, "The three powers that appear in him in almost naked severity are intellect, conscience and will."

His memorial looms large across the pages of history, in the governments of our nation, in the great men whose lives he shaped. His memory is also cherished by countless plain men who because of his logical exposition of the Scripture have been saved from skepticism, and by his tender solicitudes have been led to God.

Few critics have bothered to evaluate Idelette, his wife. It is an oversight she would have welcomed. But it was not one which Jean Calvin himself made. After her death he wrote to Pierre Viret, "My sorrow is no common one. I have lost the excellent companion of my life, who, if misfortune had come upon us, would have gladly shared with me, not merely exile in wretchedness, but death itself. . . . She has always been a faithful helper in my work. Never have I suffered the least hindrance from her."